www.EffortlessMat.

... So Much More Online!

✓ FREE Keystone Algebra I Worksheets

✓ More Math learning books!

✓ Keystone Practice Tests

✓ FREE Keystone Algebra I Course

Need a PDF version of this book?

Please visit EffortlessMath.com

10 Full Length Keystone Algebra I Practice Tests

The Practice You Need to Ace the

Keystone Algebra I Test

By

Reza Nazari

All inquiries should be addressed to:
info@effortlessMath.com

ISBN: 978-1-63719-433-1

Published by: **Effortless Math Education Inc.**

For Online Math Practice Visit www.EffortlessMath.com

Welcome to

Keystone Algebra I Prep
2024

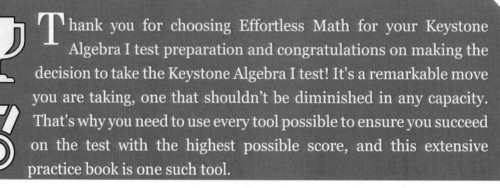

Thank you for choosing Effortless Math for your Keystone Algebra I test preparation and congratulations on making the decision to take the Keystone Algebra I test! It's a remarkable move you are taking, one that shouldn't be diminished in any capacity. That's why you need to use every tool possible to ensure you succeed on the test with the highest possible score, and this extensive practice book is one such tool.

This book will help you prepare for (and even ACE) the Keystone Algebra I final exam. As test day draws nearer, effective preparation becomes increasingly more important. Thankfully, you have this comprehensive practice book to help you get ready for the test. With this book, you can feel confident that you will be more than ready for the Keystone Algebra I test when the time comes.

First and foremost, it is important to note that this book is a practice book and not a prep book. Every test of this "self-guided math practice book" was carefully developed to ensure that you are making the most effective use of your time while preparing for the test. This up-to-date guide reflects the 2024 test guidelines and will put you on the right track to hone your math skills, overcome exam anxiety, and boost your confidence, so that you can have your best to succeed on the Keystone Algebra I test.

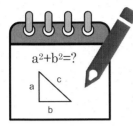

This practice book will:

☑ Explain the format of the Keystone Algebra I test.

☑ Describe specific test-taking strategies that you can use on the test.

☑ Provide Keystone Algebra I test-taking tips.

☑ Help you identify the areas in which you need to concentrate your study time.

☑ Offer Keystone Algebra I questions and explanations to help you develop the basic math skills.

☑ Give **realistic and full-length practice tests** (featuring new question types) with detailed answers to help you measure your exam readiness and build confidence.

This practice book contains 10 practice tests to help you succeed on the Keystone Algebra I test. You'll get in-depth instructions on every math topic as well as tips and techniques on how to answer each question type. You'll also get plenty of practice questions to boost your test-taking confidence.

In addition, in the following pages you'll find:

➢ **How to Use This Book Effectively** – This section provides you with step-by-step instructions on how to get the most out of this comprehensive practice book.

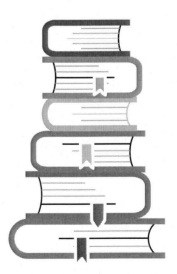

➢ **How to study for the Keystone Algebra I Test** – A six-step study program has been developed to help you make the best use of this book and prepare for your Keystone Algebra I test. Here you'll find tips and strategies to guide your study program and help you understand Keystone Algebra I and how to ace the test.

➤ **Keystone Algebra I Review** – Learn everything you need to know about the Keystone Algebra I test.

➤ **Keystone Algebra I Test-Taking Strategies** – Learn how to effectively put these recommended test-taking techniques into use for improving your Keystone Algebra I score.

➤ **Test Day Tips** – Review these tips to make sure you will do your best when the big day comes.

Effortless Math's Keystone Algebra I Online Center

Effortless Math Online Keystone Algebra I Center offers a complete study program, including the following:

✓ Step-by-step instructions on how to prepare for the Keystone Algebra I test

✓ Numerous Keystone Algebra I

✓ worksheets to help you measure your math skills

✓ Complete list of Keystone Algebra I formulas

✓ Video lessons for all Keystone Algebra I topics

✓ Full-length Keystone Algebra I practice tests

✓ And much more…

No Registration Required.

Visit effortlessmath.com/KeystoneAlgebra1 to find your online Keystone Algebra I resources.

How to Use This Book Effectively

Look no further when you need a practice book to improve your math skills to succeed on the math portion of the Keystone Algebra I test. Each section of this comprehensive practice book will provide you with the knowledge, tools, and understanding needed to succeed on the test.

It's imperative that you understand each practice question before moving onto another one, as that's the way to guarantee your success. Each practice test provides you with a step-by-step guide of every question to better understand the content that will be on the test. To get the best possible results from this book:

➢ **Begin studying long before your test date**. This provides you ample time to learn the different math concepts. The earlier you begin studying for the test, the sharper your skills will be. Do not procrastinate! Provide yourself with plenty of time to learn the concepts and feel comfortable that you understand them when your test date arrives.

➢ **Practice consistently**. Study Keystone Algebra I concepts at least 20 to 30 minutes a day. Remember, slow and steady wins the race, which can be applied to preparing for the Keystone Algebra I test. Instead of cramming to tackle everything at once, be patient and learn the math topics in short bursts.

➢ Whenever you get a math problem wrong, **mark it off, and review it later** to make sure you understand the concept.

➢ Once you've reviewed the book's instructions, **take a practice test** to gauge your level of readiness. Then, review your results. Read detailed answers and solutions for each question you missed.

➢ **Take another practice test** to get an idea of how ready you are to take the actual exam. Taking the practice tests will give you the confidence you need on test day. Simulate the Keystone Algebra I testing environment by sitting in a quiet room free from distraction. Make sure to clock yourself with a timer.

How to Study for the Keystone Algebra I Test

Studying for the Keystone Algebra I test can be a really daunting and boring task. What's the best way to go about it? Is there a certain study method that works better than others? Well, studying for the Keystone Algebra I can be done effectively. The following six-step program has been designed to make preparing for the Keystone Algebra I test more efficient and less overwhelming.

Step **1** - Create a study plan.
Step **2** - Choose your study resources.
Step **3** - Review, Learn, Practice.
Step **4** - Learn and practice test-taking strategies.
Step **5** - Learn the Keystone Algebra I Test format and take practice tests.
Step **6** - Analyze your performance.

STEP 1: Create a Study Plan

It's always easier to get things done when you have a plan. Creating a study plan for the Keystone Algebra I test can help you to stay on track with your studies. It's important to sit down and prepare a study plan with what works with your life, work, and any other obligations you may have. Devote enough time each day to studying. It's also a great 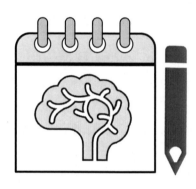 idea to break down each section of the exam into blocks and study one concept at a time.

It's important to understand that there is no "right" way to create a study plan. Your study plan will be personalized based on your specific needs and learning style. Follow these guidelines to create an effective study plan for your Keystone Algebra I test:

★ **Analyze your learning style and study habits** – Everyone has a different learning style. It is essential to embrace your individuality and the unique way you learn. Think about what works and what doesn't work for you. Do you prefer Keystone Algebra I prep books or a combination of textbooks and video

lessons? Does it work better for you if you study every night for thirty minutes or is it more effective to study in the morning before going to work?

★ **Evaluate your schedule** – Review your current schedule and find out how much time you can consistently devote to Keystone Algebra I study.

★ **Develop a schedule** – Now it's time to add your study schedule to your calendar like any other obligation. Schedule time for study, practice, and review. Plan out which topic you will study on which day to ensure that you're devoting enough time to each concept. Develop a study plan that is mindful, realistic, and flexible.

★ **Stick to your schedule** – A study plan is only effective when it is followed consistently. You should try to develop a study plan that you can follow for the length of your study program.

★ **Evaluate your study plan and adjust as needed** – Sometimes you need to adjust your plan when you have new commitments. Check in with yourself regularly to make sure that you're not falling behind in your study plan. Remember, the most important thing is sticking to your plan. Your study plan is all about helping you be more productive. If you find that your study plan is not as effective as you want, don't get discouraged. It's okay to make changes as you figure out what works best for you.

STEP 2: Choose Your Study Resources

There are numerous textbooks and online resources available for the Keystone Algebra I test, and it may not be clear where to begin. Don't worry! Effortless Math's Keystone Algebra I online center provides everything you need to fully prepare for your Keystone Algebra I test. In addition to the practice tests in this book, you can also use

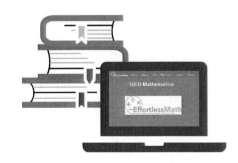

Effortless Math's online resources. (Video lessons, worksheets, formulas, etc.)

Simply visit EffortlessMath.com/KeystoneAlgebra1 to find your online Keystone Algebra I resources.

STEP 3: Review, Learn, Practice

Effortless Math's Keystone Algebra I course breaks down each subject into specific skills or content areas. For instance, the percent concept is separated into different topics–percent calculation, percent increase and decrease, percent problems, etc. Use our online resources to help you go over all key math concepts and topics on the Keystone Algebra I test.

As you review each concept, take notes or highlight the concepts you would like to go over again in the future. If you're unfamiliar with a topic or something is difficult for you, do additional research on it. For each math topic, plenty of instructions, step-by-step guides, and examples are provided to ensure you get a good grasp of the material. You can also find video lessons on the Effortless Math website for each Keystone Algebra I concept.

Quickly review the topics you do understand to get a brush-up of the material. Be sure to use the worksheets and do the practice questions provided on the Effortless Math's online center to measure your understanding of the concepts.

STEP 4: Learn and Practice Test-taking Strategies

In the following sections, you will find important test-taking strategies and tips that can help you earn extra points. You'll learn how to think strategically and when to guess if you don't know the answer to a question. Using Keystone Algebra I test-taking strategies and tips can help you raise your score and do well on the test. Apply test taking strategies on the practice tests to help you boost your confidence.

STEP 5: Learn the Keystone Algebra I Test Format and Take Practice Tests

The Keystone Algebra I Test Review section provides information about the structure of the Keystone Algebra I test. Read this section to learn more about the Keystone Algebra I test structure, different test sections, the number of questions in each section, and the section time limits. When you have a prior understanding of the test format and different types of Keystone Algebra I questions, you'll feel more confident when you take the actual exam.

Once you have read through the instructions and lessons and feel like you are ready to go – take advantage of the full-length Keystone Algebra I practice tests available in this book. Use the practice tests to sharpen your skills and build confidence.

The Keystone Algebra I practice tests offered in the book are formatted similarly to the actual Keystone Algebra I test. When you take each practice test, try to simulate actual testing conditions. To take the practice tests, sit in a quiet space, time yourself, and work through as many of the questions as time allows. The practice tests are followed by detailed answer explanations to help you find your weak areas, learn from your mistakes, and raise your Keystone Algebra I score.

STEP 6: Analyze Your Performance

After taking the practice tests, look over the answer keys and explanations to learn which questions you answered correctly and which you did not. Never be discouraged if you make a few mistakes. See them as a learning opportunity. This will highlight your strengths and weaknesses.

You can use the results to determine if you need additional practice or if you are ready to take the actual Keystone Algebra I test.

Looking for more?

Visit effortlessmath.com/KeystoneAlgebra1 to find hundreds of Keystone Algebra I worksheets, video tutorials, practice tests, Keystone Algebra I formulas, and much more.

Or scan this QR code.

No Registration Required.

Keystone Algebra I Test Review

The Keystone Exams are a set of end-of-course assessments administered in the state of Pennsylvania, United States. These exams are designed to measure a student's proficiency in specific subject areas aligned with Pennsylvania's Core Standards. The primary purpose of the Keystone Exams is to evaluate the effectiveness of the educational programs and to ensure students are prepared for post-secondary education and the workforce.

The Keystone Exams cover various subjects, such as:

1. Algebra I
2. Literature
3. Biology

Some school districts may also administer optional exams in subjects like Geometry, Algebra II, Chemistry, U.S. History, World History, and Civics and Government.

The exams are typically administered to high school students at the end of the corresponding course. Students are required to demonstrate proficiency in each of the tested subjects to meet the state's graduation requirements. In case a student does not pass a Keystone Exam, they may be provided with remedial instruction and additional opportunities to retake the test.

The results of the Keystone Exams are used for multiple purposes, including:

1. Assessing individual student performance
2. Evaluating the effectiveness of schools and districts
3. Identifying areas for improvement in instruction and curriculum
4. Meeting federal and state accountability requirements

In summary, the Keystone end-of-course tests are a set of standardized assessments used in Pennsylvania to measure student proficiency in specific subjects and ensure the quality of education provided by the state's schools.

ASSESSMENT ANCHOR

A1.1.1 Operations with Real Numbers and Expressions

Anchor Descriptor	Eligible Content	Enhanced Standard
A1.1.1.1 Represent and/or use numbers in equivalent forms (e.g., integers, fractions, decimals, percents, square roots, and exponents).	A1.1.1.1.1 Compare and/or order any real numbers. Note: Rational and irrational may be mixed.	2.1. A1. A
	A1.1.1.1.2 Simplify square roots (e.g., $\sqrt{24} = 2\sqrt{6}$).	2.1. A1. A

Anchor Descriptor	Eligible Content	Enhanced Standard
A1.1.1.2 Apply number theory concepts to show relationships between real numbers in problem-solving settings.	A1.1.1.2.1 Find the Greatest Common Factor (GCF) and/or the Least Common Multiple (LCM) for sets of monomials.	2.1. A1. E

Anchor Descriptor	Eligible Content	Enhanced Standard
A1.1.1.3 Use exponents, roots, and/or absolute values to solve problems.	A1.1.1.3.1 Simplify/evaluate expressions involving properties/laws of exponents, roots, and/or absolute values to solve problems. Note: Exponents should be integers from -10 to 10.	2.2. A1. C

Anchor Descriptor	Eligible Content	Enhanced Standard
A1.1.1.4 Use estimation strategies in problem-solving situations.	A1.1.1.4.1 Use estimation to solve problems.	2.2. A1. C

Anchor Descriptor	Eligible Content	Enhanced Standard
A1.1.1.5 Simplify expressions involving polynomials.	A1.1.1.5.1 Add, subtract, and/or multiply polynomial expressions (express answers in simplest form).	2.8. A1. B

	Note: Nothing larger than a binomial multiplied by a trinomial.	
	A1.1.1.5.2 Factor algebraic expressions, including difference of squares and trinomials. Note: Trinomials are limited to the form $ax^2 + bx + c$ where a is equal to 1 after factoring out all monomial factors.	2.1. A1. B
	A1.1.1.5.3 Simplify/reduce a rational algebraic expression.	2.8. A1. B

ASSESSMENT ANCHOR

A1.1.2 Linear Equations

Anchor Descriptor	Eligible Content	Enhanced Standard
A1.1.2.1 Write, solve, and/or graph linear equations using various methods.	A1.1.2.1.1 Write, solve, and/or apply a linear equation (including problem situations).	2.1. A1. F 2.8. A1. E 2.8. A1. F
	A1.1.2.1.2 Use and/or identify an algebraic property to justify any step in an equation-solving process. Note: Linear equations only.	2.1. A1. F
	A1.1.2.1.3 Interpret solutions to problems in the context of the problem situation. Note: Linear equations only.	2.8. A1. F
Anchor Descriptor	**Eligible Content**	**Enhanced Standard**
A1.1.2.2 Write, solve, and/or graph systems of linear equations using various methods.	A1.1.2.2.1 Write and/or solve a system of linear equations (including problem situations) using graphing, substitution, and/or elimination.	2.8. A1. E 2.8. A1. F

	Note: Limit systems to two linear equations.	
	A1.1.2.2.2 Interpret solutions to problems in the context of the problem situation. Note: Limit systems to two linear equations.	2.8. A1. F

ASSESSMENT ANCHOR

A1.1.3 Linear Inequalities

Anchor Descriptor	Eligible Content	Enhanced Standard
A1.1.3.1 Write, solve, and/or graph linear inequalities using various methods.	A1.1.3.1.1 Write or solve compound inequalities and/or graph their solution sets on a number line (may include absolute value inequalities).	2.1. A1. F 2.8. A1. E 2.8. A1. F
	A1.1.3.1.2 Identify or graph the solution set to a linear inequality on a number line.	2.8. A1. B
	A1.1.3.1.3 Interpret solutions to problems in the context of the problem situation. Note: Limit to linear inequalities.	2.8. A1. F
Anchor Descriptor	**Eligible Content**	**Enhanced Standard**
A1.1.3.2 Write, solve, and/or graph systems of linear inequalities using various methods.	A1.1.3.2.1 Write and/or solve a system of linear inequalities using graphing. Note: Limit systems to two linear inequalities.	2.8. A1. E 2.8. A1. F
	A1.1.3.2.2 Interpret solutions to problems in the context of the problem situation. Note: Limit systems to two linear inequalities.	2.8. A1. F

ASSESSMENT ANCHOR

A1.2.1 Functions

Anchor Descriptor	Eligible Content	Enhanced Standard
A1.2.1.1 Analyze and/or use patterns or relations.	A1.2.1.1.1 Analyze a set of data for the existence of a pattern and represent the pattern algebraically and/or graphically.	2.8. A1. C
	A1.2.1.1.2 Determine whether a relation is a function, given a set of points or a graph.	2.8. A1. D
	A1.2.1.1.3 Identify the domain or range of a relation (may be presented as ordered pairs, a graph, or a table).	2.8. A1. D
Anchor Descriptor	Eligible Content	Enhanced Standard
A1.2.1.2 Interpret and/or use linear functions and their equations, graphs, or tables.	A1.2.1.2.1 Create, interpret, and/or use the equation, graph, or table of a linear function.	2.8. A1. D
	A1.2.1.2.2 Translate from one representation of a linear function to another (i.e., graph, table, and equation).	2.8. A1. D

ASSESSMENT ANCHOR

A1.2.2 Coordinate Geometry

Anchor Descriptor	Eligible Content	Enhanced Standard
A1.2.2.1 Describe, compute, and/or use the rate of change (slope) of a line.	A1.2.2.1.1 Identify, describe, and/or use constant rates of change.	2.11. A1. B
	A1.2.2.1.2 Apply the concept of linear rate of change (slope) to solve problems.	2.9. A1. C
	A1.2.2.1.3 Write or identify a linear equation when given	2.9. A1. C

	• the graph of the line,	
	• two points on the line, or	
	• the slope and a point on the line.	
	Note: Linear equation may be in point-slope, standard, and/or slope-intercept form.	
	A1.2.2.1.4 Determine the slope and/or y-intercept represented by a linear equation or graph.	2.8. A1. D
Anchor Descriptor	**Eligible Content**	**Enhanced** **Standard**
A1.2.2.2 Analyze and/or interpret data on a scatter plot.	A1.2.2.2.1 Draw, identify, find, and/or write an equation for a line of best fit for a scatter plot.	2.6. A1. C

ASSESSMENT ANCHOR **A1. 2. 3 Data Analysis**		
Anchor Descriptor	**Eligible Content**	**Enhanced** **Standard**
A1.2.3.1 Use measures of dispersion to describe a set of data.	A1.2.3.1.1 Calculate and/or interpret the range, quartiles, and interquartile range of data.	2.6. A1. C
Anchor Descriptor	**Eligible Content**	**Enhanced** **Standard**
A1.2.3.2 Use data displays in problem-solving settings and/or to make predictions.	A1.2.3.2.1 Estimate or calculate to make predictions based on a circle, line, bar graph, measures of central tendency, or other representations.	2.6. A1. E
	A1.2.3.2.2 Analyze data, make predictions, and/or answer questions based on	2.6. A1. E

	displayed data (box-and whisker plots, stem-and-leaf plots, scatter plots, measures of central tendency, or other representations).	
	A1.2.3.2.3 Make predictions using the equations or graphs of best-fit lines of scatter plots.	2.6. A1. E
Anchor Descriptor	**Eligible Content**	**Enhanced Standard**
A1.2.3.3 Apply probability to practical situations.	A1.2.3.3.1 Find probabilities for compound events (e.g., find probability of red and blue, find probability of red or blue) and represent as a fraction, decimal, or percent.	2.7. A1. A

Keystone Algebra I Test-Taking Strategies

Here are some test-taking strategies that you can use to maximize your performance and results on the Keystone Algebra I test.

#1: USE THIS APPROACH TO ANSWER EVERY KEYSTONE ALGEBRA I QUESTION

- Review the question to identify keywords and important information.

- Translate the keywords into math operations so you can solve the problem.

- Review the answer choices. What are the differences between answer choices?

- Draw or label a diagram if needed.

- Try to find patterns.

- Find the right method to answer the question. Use straightforward math, plug in numbers, or test the answer choices (backsolving).

- Double-check your work.

#2: USE EDUCATED GUESSING

This approach is applicable to the problems you understand to some degree but cannot solve using straightforward math. In such cases, try to filter out as many answer choices as possible before picking an answer. In cases where you don't have a clue about what a certain problem entails, don't waste any time trying to eliminate answer choices. Just choose one randomly before moving onto the next question.

As you can ascertain, direct solutions are the most optimal approach. Carefully read through the question, determine what the solution is using the math you have learned before, then coordinate the answer with one of the choices available to you. Are you stumped? Make your best guess, then move on.

Don't leave any fields empty! Even if you're unable to work out a problem, strive to answer it. Take a guess if you have to. You will not lose points by getting an answer wrong, though you may gain a point by getting it correct!

#3 : Ballpark

A ballpark answer is a rough approximation. When we become overwhelmed by calculations and figures, we end up making silly mistakes. A decimal that is moved by one unit can change an answer from right to wrong, regardless of the number of steps that you went through to get it. That's where ballparking can play a big part.

If you think you know what the correct answer may be (even if it's just a ballpark answer), you'll usually have the ability to eliminate a couple of choices. While answer choices are usually based on the average student error and/or values that are closely tied, you will still be able to weed out choices that are way far afield. Try to find answers that aren't in the proverbial ballpark when you're looking for a wrong answer on a multiple-choice question. This is an optimal approach to eliminating answers to a problem.

#4 : Backsolving

A majority of questions on the Keystone Algebra I test will be in multiple-choice format. Many test-takers prefer multiple-choice questions, as at least the answer is right there. You'll typically have four answers to pick from. You simply need to figure out which one is correct. Usually, the best way to go about doing so is "backsolving."

As mentioned earlier, direct solutions are the most optimal approach to answering a question. Carefully read through a problem, calculate a solution, then correspond the answer with one of the choices displayed in front of you. If you can't calculate a solution, your next best approach involves "backsolving."

When backsolving a problem, contrast one of your answer options against the problem you are asked, then see which of them is most relevant. More often than not, answer choices are listed in ascending or descending order. In such cases, try out the choices B or C. If it's not correct, you can go either down or up from there.

#5 : PLUGGING IN NUMBERS

"Plugging in numbers" is a strategy that can be applied to a wide range of different math problems on the Keystone Algebra I test. This approach is typically used to simplify a challenging question so that it is more understandable. By using the strategy carefully, you can find the answer without too much trouble.

The concept is fairly straightforward–replace unknown variables in a problem with certain values. When selecting a number, consider the following:

- Choose a number that's basic (just not too basic). Generally, you should avoid choosing 1 (or even 0). A decent choice is 2.

- Try not to choose a number that is displayed in the problem.

- Make sure you keep your numbers different if you need to choose at least two of them.

- More often than not, choosing numbers merely lets you filter out some of your answer choices. As such, don't just go with the first choice that gives you the right answer.

- If several answers seem correct, then you'll need to choose another value and try again. This time, though, you'll just need to check choices that haven't been eliminated yet.

- If your question contains fractions, then a potential right answer may involve either an LCD (least common denominator) or an LCD multiple.

- 100 is the number you should choose when you are dealing with problems involving percentages.

Keystone Algebra I – Test Day Tips

After practicing and reviewing all the math concepts you've been taught, and taking some Keystone Algebra I practice tests, you'll be prepared for test day. Consider the following tips to be extra-ready come test time.

Before Your Test

What to do the night before:

■ **Relax!** One day before your test, study lightly or skip studying altogether. You shouldn't attempt to learn something new, either. There are plenty of reasons why studying the evening before a big test can work against you. Put it this way–a marathoner wouldn't go out for a sprint before the day of a big race. Mental marathoners–such as yourself–should not study for any more than one hour 24 hours before a Keystone Algebra I test. That's because your brain requires some rest to be at its best. The night before your exam, spend some time with family or friends, or read a book.

■ **Avoid bright screens** - You'll have to get some good shuteye the night before your test. Bright screens (such as the ones coming from your laptop, TV, or mobile device) should be avoided altogether. Staring at such a screen will keep your brain up, making it hard to drift asleep at a reasonable hour.

■ **Make sure your dinner is healthy** - The meal that you have for dinner should be nutritious. Be sure to drink plenty of water as well. Load up on your complex carbohydrates, much like a marathon runner would do. Pasta, rice, and potatoes are ideal options here, as are vegetables and protein sources.

■ **Get your bag ready for test day** - The night prior to your test, pack your bag with your stationery, admissions pass, ID, and any other gear that you need. Keep the bag right by your front door.

■ **Make plans to reach the testing site** - Before going to sleep, ensure that you understand precisely how you will arrive at the site of the test. If parking is something you'll have to find first, plan for it. If you're dependent on public transit, then review the schedule. You should also make sure that the train/bus/subway/streetcar you use will be running. Find out about road closures as well. If a parent or friend is accompanying you, ensure that they understand what steps they have to take as well.

The Day of the Test

■ **Get up reasonably early, but not too early.**

■ **Have breakfast** - Breakfast improves your concentration, memory, and mood. As such, make sure the breakfast that you eat in the morning is healthy. The last thing you want to be is distracted by a grumbling tummy. If it's not your own stomach making those noises, another test taker close to you might be instead. Prevent discomfort or embarrassment by consuming a healthy breakfast. Bring a snack with you if you think you'll need it.

■ **Follow your daily routine** - Do you watch Good Morning America each morning while getting ready for the day? Don't break your usual habits on the day of the test. Likewise, if coffee isn't something you drink in the morning, then don't take up the habit hours before your test. Routine consistency lets you concentrate on the main objective–doing the best you can on your test.

■ **Wear layers** - Dress yourself up in comfortable layers. You should be ready for any kind of internal temperature. If it gets too warm during the test, take a layer off.

■ **Get there on time** - The last thing you want to do is get to the test site late. Rather, you should be there 45 minutes prior to the start of the test. Upon your arrival, try not to hang out with anybody who is nervous. Any anxious energy they exhibit shouldn't influence you.

■ **Leave the books at home** - No books should be brought to the test site. If you start developing anxiety before the test, books could encourage you to do some last-minute studying, which will only hinder you. Keep the books far away–better yet, leave them at home.

■ **Make your voice heard** - If something is off, speak to a proctor. If medical attention is needed or if you'll require anything, consult the proctor prior to the start of the test. Any doubts you have should be clarified. You should be entering the test site with a state of mind that is completely clear.

■ **Have faith in yourself** - When you feel confident, you will be able to perform at your best. When you are waiting for the test to begin, envision yourself receiving an outstanding result. Try to see yourself as someone who knows all the answers, no matter what the questions are. A lot of athletes tend to use this technique–particularly before a big competition. Your expectations will be reflected by your performance.

During your test

- **Be calm and breathe deeply** - You need to relax before the test, and some deep breathing will go a long way to help you do that. Be confident and calm. You got this. Everybody feels a little stressed out just before an evaluation of any kind is set to begin. Learn some effective breathing exercises. Spend a minute meditating before the test starts. Filter out any negative thoughts you have. Exhibit confidence when having such thoughts.

- **Concentrate on the test** - Refrain from comparing yourself to anyone else. You shouldn't be distracted by the people near you or random noise. Concentrate exclusively on the test. If you find yourself irritated by surrounding noises, earplugs can be used to block sounds off close to you. Don't forget–the test is going to last several hours if you're taking more than one subject of the test. Some of that time will be dedicated to brief sections. Concentrate on the specific section you are working on during a particular moment. Do not let your mind wander off to upcoming or previous sections.

- **Try to answer each question individually** - Focus only on the question you are working on. Use one of the test-taking strategies to solve the problem. If you aren't able to come up with an answer, don't get frustrated. Simply skip that question, then move onto the next one.

- **Don't forget to breathe!** Whenever you notice your mind wandering, your stress levels boosting, or frustration brewing, take a thirty-second break. Shut your eyes, drop your pencil, breathe deeply, and let your shoulders relax. You will end up being more productive when you allow yourself to relax for a moment.

- **Optimize your breaks** - When break time comes, use the restroom, have a snack, and reactivate your energy for the subsequent section. Doing some stretches can help stimulate your blood flow.

After your test

- **Take it easy** - You will need to set some time aside to relax and decompress once the test has concluded. There is no need to stress yourself out about what you could've said, or what you may have done wrong. At this point, there's nothing you can do about it. Your energy and time would be better spent on something that will bring you happiness for the remainder of your day.

Contents

Time to Test

Time to refine your algebra skills with a practice test

Take an Keystone Algebra I test to simulate the test day experience. After you've finished, score your test using the answer keys.

Before You Start

- You'll need a pencil and a calculator to take the test.

- For multiple questions, there are five possible answers. Choose which one is best.

- It's okay to guess. There is no penalty for wrong answers.

- Use the answer sheet provided to record your answers.

- **Scientific calculator is permitted for Keystone Algebra I Test.**

- After you've finished the test, review the answer key to see where you went wrong.

Good Luck!

Keystone Algebra I Practice Test 1

2024

Two Parts

Total number of questions: 27

Part 1: 23 questions

Part 2: 4 questions

Total time: No time limit

1

Keystone Algebra I Practice Test Answer Sheet

Remove (or photocopy) this answer sheet and use it to complete the practice test.

Keystone Algebra I Practice Test 1 Answer Sheet

1	Ⓐ Ⓑ Ⓒ Ⓓ		21	Ⓐ Ⓑ Ⓒ Ⓓ
2	Ⓐ Ⓑ Ⓒ Ⓓ		22	Ⓐ Ⓑ Ⓒ Ⓓ
3	Ⓐ Ⓑ Ⓒ Ⓓ		23	Ⓐ Ⓑ Ⓒ Ⓓ
4	Ⓐ Ⓑ Ⓒ Ⓓ		24	
5	Ⓐ Ⓑ Ⓒ Ⓓ		25	
6	Ⓐ Ⓑ Ⓒ Ⓓ		26	
7	Ⓐ Ⓑ Ⓒ Ⓓ		27	
8	Ⓐ Ⓑ Ⓒ Ⓓ			
9	Ⓐ Ⓑ Ⓒ Ⓓ			
10	Ⓐ Ⓑ Ⓒ Ⓓ			
11	Ⓐ Ⓑ Ⓒ Ⓓ			
12	Ⓐ Ⓑ Ⓒ Ⓓ			
13	Ⓐ Ⓑ Ⓒ Ⓓ			
14	Ⓐ Ⓑ Ⓒ Ⓓ			
15	Ⓐ Ⓑ Ⓒ Ⓓ			
16	Ⓐ Ⓑ Ⓒ Ⓓ			
17	Ⓐ Ⓑ Ⓒ Ⓓ			
18	Ⓐ Ⓑ Ⓒ Ⓓ			
19	Ⓐ Ⓑ Ⓒ Ⓓ			
20	Ⓐ Ⓑ Ⓒ Ⓓ			

Keystone Algebra I Practice Test 1

2024

Part 1

Total number of questions: 23

Total time: No time limit

You may use a calculator on this part.

3

1) Which one is not true for the function $g(x) = 3x^2 - 6x$?

   A. The axis of symmetry of the function g is $x = 1$.

   B. The zeros are 0 and 2.

   C. The factors of g are x and $x - 2$.

   D. The axis of symmetry of the function g is $y = -3$.

2) Which of the following is a factor of $12x^8 - 21x^4 + 3x^3$?

   A. $4x^5 - 7x + 1$

   B. $x - 1$

   C. $3x + 1$

   D. $4x^5 - 7x^2$

3) Write the equation of a horizontal line that goes through the point $(-5, 12)$.

   A. $y = 12$

   B. $x = 12$

   C. $y = -5$

   D. $x = -5$

4) A part of an exponential function is graphed on the grid.

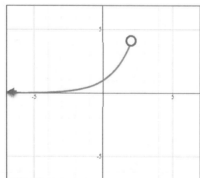

   Which inequality best represents the range of the part shown?

   A. $0 \le y$

   B. $-\infty < x < 2$

   C. $x \le 2$

   D. $0 < y < 4$

5) $(7x + 2y)(5x + 2y) =?$

 A. $35x^2 + 24xy + 4y^2$

 B. $2x^2 + 4xy + 2y^2$

 C. $7x^2 + 14xy + y^2$

 D. $12x^2 + 14xy + 4y$

6) Which function is equivalent to $f(x) = 5x^2 - 30x - 4$?

 A. $f(x) = 5(x - 3)^2 + 49$

 B. $f(x) = 5(x + 3)^2 - 49$

 C. $f(x) = 5(x - 3)^2 - 49$

 D. $f(x) = 5(x - 49)^2 - 3$

7) Which graph does not represent y as a function of x?

A.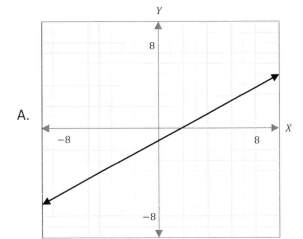

B.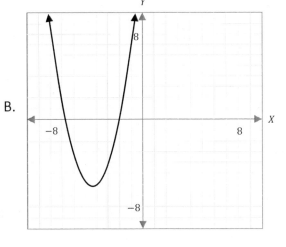

C.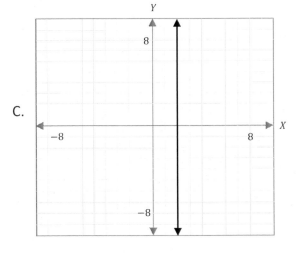

D.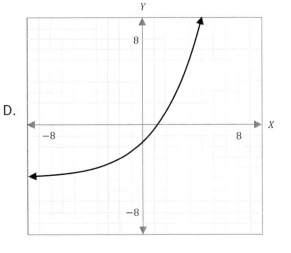

8) Which graph best represents the solution set of $x < 3 - 2y$?

A.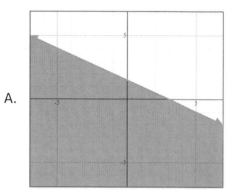

B.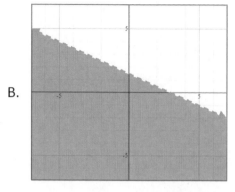

C.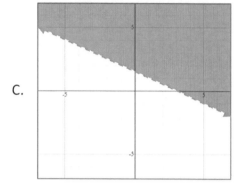

D.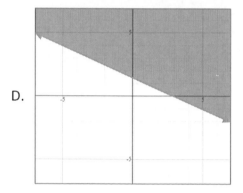

9) Two characteristics of quadratic function f are given.

   ○   The axis of symmetry of the graph of f is $x = 1$.

   ○   Function f has exactly two zeros.

   Based on this information, which graph could represent f?

A.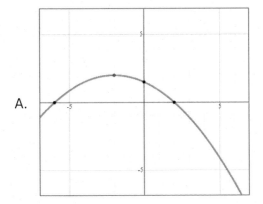

B.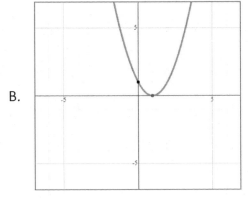

C.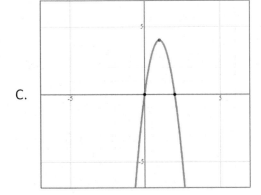

D.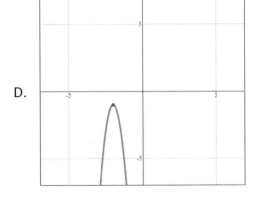

10) A college student has two different jobs. Her combined work schedules consist of no more than 192 hours in the month.

Which graph best represents the solution set for all possible combinations of x, the number of hours she worked at her first job, and y, the number of hours she worked at her second job, in one month?

A.
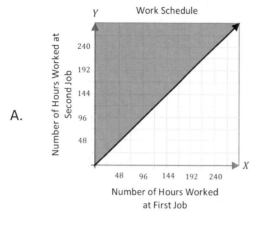

B.
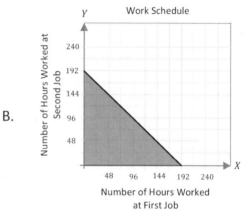

C.
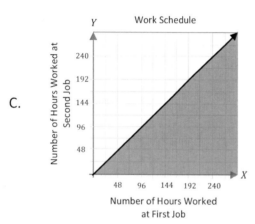

D.
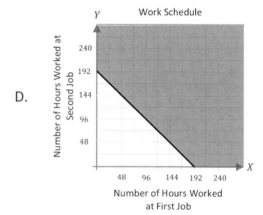

11) On the page of an influencer, the number of followers and the number of feedback on each post by users are collected in the following table. A linear function can be used to show the data.

Number of Followers on the Page, x	Number of Feedback of each Post, y
480	12
1480	37
840	21
2600	63
3280	82
1280	32

Based on the table, what is the best prediction of the number of feedback for each post if the number of followers reaches 4,000 people on the page?

A. 63

B. 82

C. 100

D. 114

12) The graph shows the linear relationship between the maximum length of the highway line per foot that can be painted and the number of gallons of paint used.

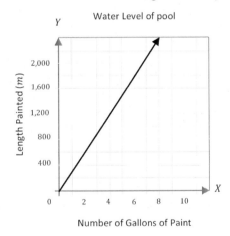

Which of these best represents the rate of change of the maximum length painted with respect to the number of gallons of paint used?

A. $200\,m/gal$

B. $\frac{1}{200}m/gal$

C. $300\,m/gal$

D. $\frac{1}{300}m/gal$

13) The graph of $f(x) = x^2$ is transformed to create the graph of $g(x) = 0.35f(x)$. Which graph best represents f and g?

A.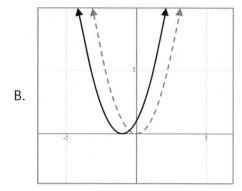

B.

C.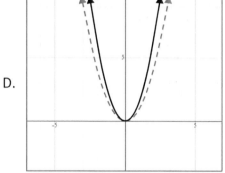

D.

14) What is the ratio of the minimum value to the maximum value of the following function?
$$f(x) = -3x + 1, -2 \leq x \leq 3$$

A. $-\dfrac{8}{7}$

B. $\dfrac{7}{8}$

C. $-\dfrac{7}{8}$

D. $\dfrac{8}{7}$

15) A system of linear equations is represented by line t and line g. A table representing some points on line t and the graph of line g is shown.

Which system of equations is best represented by lines t and g?

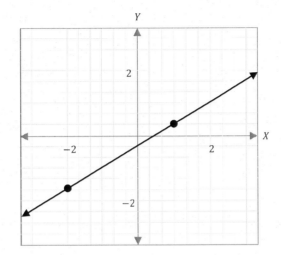

Line t

x	-1	1	7
y	4	2	-4

A. $y = \frac{2}{3}x - \frac{1}{3}$
   $y = 3 - x$

B. $2x - 3y = 1$
   $x + y = 3$

C. $y = \frac{3}{2}x - 3$
   $y = \frac{1}{3} - x$

D. $2x - 3y = 1$
   $x - y = 3$

16) In 1999, the average worker's income increased by \$2,000 per year starting from a \$26,000 annual salary. Which equation represents income greater than average?
(I = income, x = number of years after 1999)

A. $I > 2,000x + 26,000$

B. $I > -2,000x + 26,000$

C. $I < -2,000x + 26,000$

D. $I < 2,000x - 26,000$

17) Solve: $\dfrac{3x+6}{x+5} \times \dfrac{x+5}{x+2} =$.

A. 1

B. 2

C. 3

D. $\dfrac{x+5}{x+2}$

18) The following graph shows the number of bacteria in a laboratory sample in a few hours. Based on this information, which function best shows the number of bacteria x per hour?

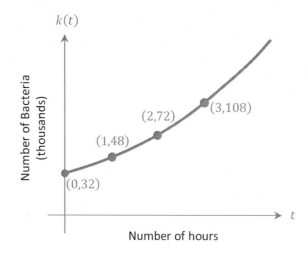

A. $y = 48(0.67)^x$

B. $y = 32(1.5)^x$

C. $y = 1.5(32)^x$

D. $y = 0.67(48)^x$

19) Simplify $\frac{6}{\sqrt{12} - 3}$.

A. $\sqrt{12} + 3$

B. 2

C. $2(\sqrt{12} + 3)$

D. $2\sqrt{12}$

20) A basketball player throws a ball toward the basketball net. The graph shows the height in yards of the basketball ball above the ground as a quadratic function of x, the horizontal distance in yards of the basketball ball from the hands of the player.

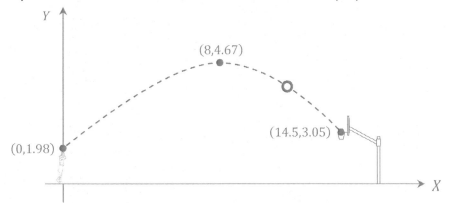

What is the domain of the function for this solution?

A. $0 \leq x \leq 14.5$

B. $0 \leq y \leq 4.67$

C. $1.98 \leq y \leq 4.67$

D. $1.98 \leq x \leq 14.5$

21) Which of the following numbers is NOT a solution to the inequality $2x - 5 \geq 3x - 1$?

A. -2

B. -4

C. -5

D. -8

22) Which expression is equivalent to $9n^2 - 36$?

A. $(3n - 6)(3n - 6)$

B. $9(n - 4)$

C. $9n(n - 4)$

D. $9(n - 2)(n + 2)$

23) What is the value of the y −intercept of the graph of $g(x) = 25(1.2)^{x+1}$?

A. 20

B. 25

C. 30

D. 1

STOP
This is the End of this Section.

Keystone Algebra I Practice Test 1

2024

Part 2

Total number of questions: 4

Total time: No time limit

You may use a calculator on this part.

15

24) What is the value of the y −intercept of the graph $f(x) = 11.5(0.8)^x$?

25) What is the solution to $7x - 5 = 16 + 4x$?

26) The graph of quadratic function f is shown on the grid.

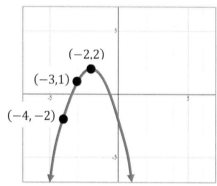

What is the y −intercept of the graph of f?

27) What is the negative solution to $2x^3 - x^2 - 6x = 0$?

Keystone Algebra I Practice Test 2

2024

Two Parts

Total number of questions: 27

Part 1: 23 questions

Part 2: 4 questions

Total time: No time limit

19

Keystone Algebra I Practice Test Answer Sheet

Remove (or photocopy) this answer sheet and use it to complete the practice test.

Keystone Algebra I Practice Test 2 Answer Sheet

1 Ⓐ Ⓑ Ⓒ Ⓓ	21 Ⓐ Ⓑ Ⓒ Ⓓ
2 Ⓐ Ⓑ Ⓒ Ⓓ	22 Ⓐ Ⓑ Ⓒ Ⓓ
3 Ⓐ Ⓑ Ⓒ Ⓓ	23 Ⓐ Ⓑ Ⓒ Ⓓ
4 Ⓐ Ⓑ Ⓒ Ⓓ	24
5 Ⓐ Ⓑ Ⓒ Ⓓ	25
6 Ⓐ Ⓑ Ⓒ Ⓓ	26
7 Ⓐ Ⓑ Ⓒ Ⓓ	27
8 Ⓐ Ⓑ Ⓒ Ⓓ	
9 Ⓐ Ⓑ Ⓒ Ⓓ	
10 Ⓐ Ⓑ Ⓒ Ⓓ	
11 Ⓐ Ⓑ Ⓒ Ⓓ	
12 Ⓐ Ⓑ Ⓒ Ⓓ	
13 Ⓐ Ⓑ Ⓒ Ⓓ	
14 Ⓐ Ⓑ Ⓒ Ⓓ	
15 Ⓐ Ⓑ Ⓒ Ⓓ	
16 Ⓐ Ⓑ Ⓒ Ⓓ	
17 Ⓐ Ⓑ Ⓒ Ⓓ	
18 Ⓐ Ⓑ Ⓒ Ⓓ	
19 Ⓐ Ⓑ Ⓒ Ⓓ	
20 Ⓐ Ⓑ Ⓒ Ⓓ	

Keystone Algebra I Practice Test 2

2024

Part 1

Total number of questions: 23

Total time: No time limit

You may use a calculator on this part.

21

1) An influencer has two different jobs. His combined work schedules consist of less than 65 hours per week.

   Which graph best represents the solution set for all possible combinations of x, the number of hours she worked at her first job, and y, the number of hours she worked at her second job, in one week?

A.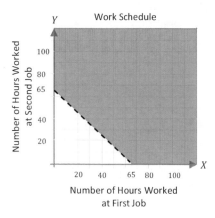

B.

C.

D.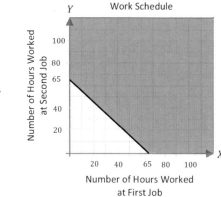

2) In the standard (x, y) coordinate plane, which of the following lines contains the points $(3, -5)$ and $(8, 15)$?

   A. $y = \frac{1}{4}x + 13$

   B. $y = -\frac{1}{4}x + 17$

   C. $y = 2x - 11$

   D. $y = 4x - 17$

3) Which of the following is equal to the expression below?

$$(5x + 2y)(2x - y)$$

    A. $2x^2 + 6xy - 2y^2$

    B. $4x^2 - 2y^2$

    C. $8x^2 + 2xy - 2y^2$

    D. $10x^2 - xy - 2y^2$

4) A quadratic function is graphed on the grid.

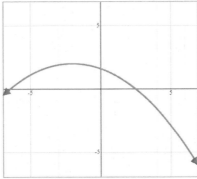

    Which answer choice best represents the domain and range of the function?

    A. Domain: All real numbers

       Range: $y \geq 2$

    B. Domain: $-7 \leq x \leq 7$

       Range: $y < 2$

    C. Domain: $y < 2$

       Range: All real numbers

    D. Domain: All real numbers

       Range: $y \leq 2$

5) What is the slope of a line that is perpendicular to the line $4x - 2y = 6$?

    A. $-\dfrac{1}{2}$

    B. -2

    C. 4

    D. 12

6) Tickets to a movie cost $12.50 for adults and $7.50 for students. A group of 12 friends purchased tickets for $125. How many student tickets did they buy?

   A. 3

   B. 5

   C. 7

   D. 8

7) Which graph best represents part of a quadratic function with a range of all real numbers less than -4?

A.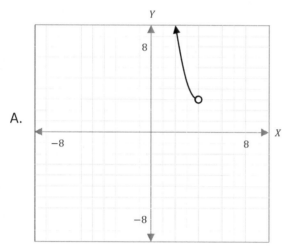

B.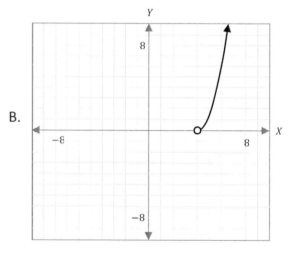

C.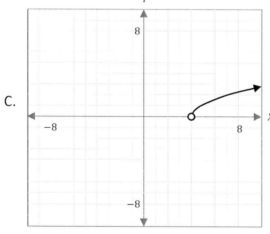

D.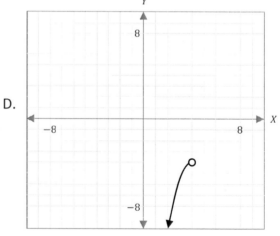

8) If the function is defined as $f(x) = bx^2 + 15$, b is a constant, and $f(2) = 35$. What is the value of $f(3)$?

   A. 25

   B. 35

   C. 60

   D. 65

9) The graph of a line is shown on the grid. The coordinates of both points indicated on the graph of the line are integers.

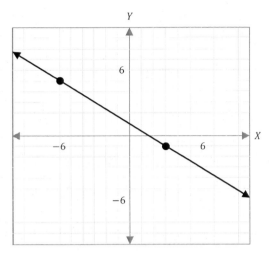

What is the rate of change of y with respect to x for this line?

A. $\frac{3}{2}$

B. $-\frac{2}{3}$

C. $-\frac{3}{2}$

D. $\frac{2}{3}$

10) What are the equation and slope of the line shown on the grid?

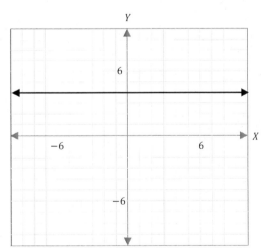

A. $x = 4$; the slope is 1.

B. $y = 4$; the slope is zero.

C. $x = 4$; the slope is 4.

D. $y = 4$; the slope is undefined.

11) In a sequence of numbers, $a_4 = 19$, $a_5 = 23$, $a_6 = 27$, $a_7 = 31$, and $a_8 = 35$. Based on this information, which equation can be used to find the nth term in the sequence, a_n?

   A. $a_n = 4n - 3$

   B. $a_n = 3n + 4$

   C. $a_n = 4n + 3$

   D. $a_n = 3n - 4$

12) A project manager is monitoring the progress of the production of a new product. The scatterplot and table show the number of weeks since the start of the production and the percentage of the residual process. A linear function can be used to model this relationship. Which function best models the data?

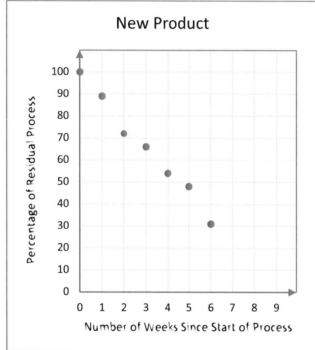

Number of Weeks Since Start of process, x	Percentage of Residual Process, y
0	100
1	89
2	72
3	66
4	54
5	48

   A. $y = 8.5x - 98.7$

   B. $y = -11.5x + 8.5$

   C. $y = 98.7x - 11.5$

   D. $y = -11.5x + 98.7$

13) Which graph best represents a system of equations that has no solution?

A.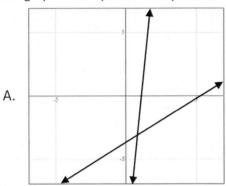

B.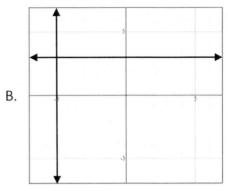

C.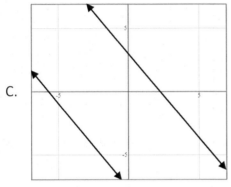

D.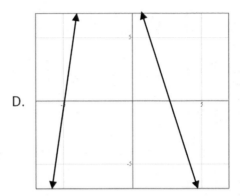

14) What is the y −intercept of the line with the equation $x - 3y = 12$?

   A. 1

   B. −2

   C. 3

   D. −4

Line L_1

x	4	8	12
y	−2	−1	0

Line L_2

x	−3	0	1
y	9	3	1

15) The tables of ordered pairs represent some points on the graphs of lines L_1 and L_2. Which system of equations is represented by lines L_1 and L_2?

   A. $3x - 4y = 24$
      $x + 2y = -6$

   B. $4x - 3y = -24$
      $x + 2y = 6$

   C. $4x - 3y = 6$
      $x - y = -24$

   D. $x - 4y = 12$
      $2x + y = 3$

16) Simplify $7x^2y^3(2x^2y)^3 =$.

   A. $14x^4y^6$

   B. $14x^8y^6$

   C. $56x^4y^6$

   D. $56x^8y^6$

17) What are the zeroes of the function $f(x) = x^3 + 7x^2 + 12x$?

   A. 0

   B. $-4, -3$

   C. $0, 2, 3$

   D. $0, -3, -4$

18) Which expression is equivalent to $0.00035 \times (1.2 \times 10^4)$?

   A. 4.2×10^{-1}

   B. 4.2

   C. 4.2×10

   D. 4.2×10^2

19) The water level of a seasonal lake was measured each day during a ten-week period. The graph shows the linear relationship between the water level of the lake in feet and the number of days the water level was measured.

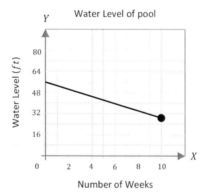

Which statement best describes the y −intercept of the graph?

   A. The water level was measured for 10 weeks.

   B. The maximum water level was 56 feet.

   C. The final water level was 30 feet.

   D. The water level decreased by 4.6 feet per week.

20) Find the axis of symmetry of the function $g(x) = -\frac{1}{8}(x-1)^2 - 3$.

    A. $y = 3$

    B. There is no axis of symmetry.

    C. $x = 1$

    D. $y = -3x + 1$

21) The initial value of a car is \$35,000. The value of the car will decrease at a rate of 20% each year.
    Which graph best models this situation?

A.
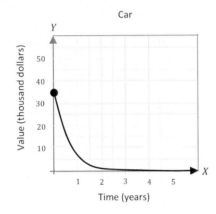

B.
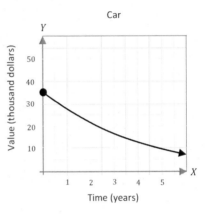

C.
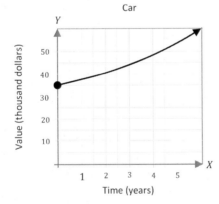

D.
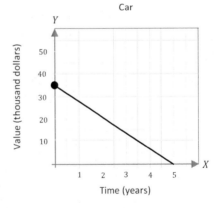

22) Which graph best represents the solution set of $5x + 2y \geq 10$?

A.
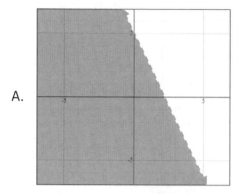

B.
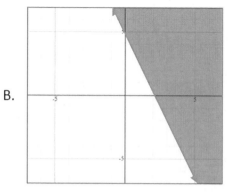

C.
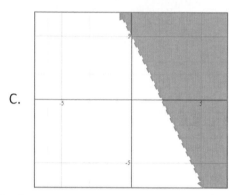

D.
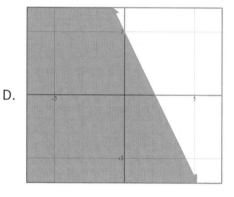

23) Which expression is equivalent to $k^2 - 17k + 66$?

    A. $(k + 6)(k + 11)$

    B. $(k - 33)(k - 2)$

    C. $(k + 33)(k + 2)$

    D. $(k - 6)(k - 11)$

STOP

This is the End of this Section.

Keystone Algebra I Practice Test 2

2024

Part 2

Total number of questions: 4

Total time: No time limit

You may use a calculator on this part.

31

24) The expression $n^{-3}(n^2)^3$ is equivalent to n^x. What is the value of x?

25) What is the positive solution to this equation?
$$6(x-1)^2 = 41 - x$$

26) Quadratic function k can be used to show the height in meters of a rocket from the ground t seconds after it was launched. The graph of the function is shown.

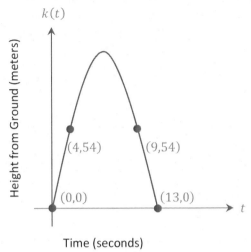

What is the maximum value of the graph of the function? (round your answer to the whole number)

27) If $x = 9$, what is the value of y in the following equation? $2y = \dfrac{2x^2}{3} + 6$

End of Keystone Algebra I Practice Test 2

Keystone Algebra I Practice Test 3

2024

Two Parts

Total number of questions: 27

Part 1: 23 questions

Part 2: 4 questions

Total time: No time limit

35

Keystone Algebra I Practice Test Answer Sheet

Remove (or photocopy) this answer sheet and use it to complete the practice test.

Keystone Algebra I Practice Test 3 Answer Sheet

1	Ⓐ Ⓑ Ⓒ Ⓓ	21	Ⓐ Ⓑ Ⓒ Ⓓ
2	Ⓐ Ⓑ Ⓒ Ⓓ	22	Ⓐ Ⓑ Ⓒ Ⓓ
3	Ⓐ Ⓑ Ⓒ Ⓓ	23	Ⓐ Ⓑ Ⓒ Ⓓ
4	Ⓐ Ⓑ Ⓒ Ⓓ	24	
5	Ⓐ Ⓑ Ⓒ Ⓓ	25	
6	Ⓐ Ⓑ Ⓒ Ⓓ	26	
7	Ⓐ Ⓑ Ⓒ Ⓓ	27	
8	Ⓐ Ⓑ Ⓒ Ⓓ		
9	Ⓐ Ⓑ Ⓒ Ⓓ		
10	Ⓐ Ⓑ Ⓒ Ⓓ		
11	Ⓐ Ⓑ Ⓒ Ⓓ		
12	Ⓐ Ⓑ Ⓒ Ⓓ		
13	Ⓐ Ⓑ Ⓒ Ⓓ		
14	Ⓐ Ⓑ Ⓒ Ⓓ		
15	Ⓐ Ⓑ Ⓒ Ⓓ		
16	Ⓐ Ⓑ Ⓒ Ⓓ		
17	Ⓐ Ⓑ Ⓒ Ⓓ		
18	Ⓐ Ⓑ Ⓒ Ⓓ		
19	Ⓐ Ⓑ Ⓒ Ⓓ		
20	Ⓐ Ⓑ Ⓒ Ⓓ		

Keystone Algebra I Practice Test 3

2024

Part 1

Total number of questions: 13

Total time: No time limit

You may use a calculator on this part.

37

1) The graph of quadratic function q is shown on the grid.

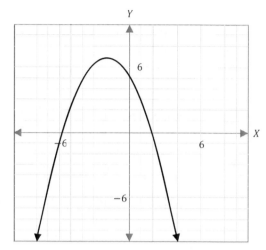

Which answer choice best represents the intercepts of the graph of q?

A. x −intercept $(-6,0)$ and $(2,0)$
   y − intercept $(0,5)$

B. x − intercept $(0,5)$
   y − intercept $(-6,0)$ and $(2,0)$

C. x − intercept $(5,0)$
   y − intercept $(0,-6)$ and $(0,2)$

D. x − intercept $(0,5)$
   y −intercept $(6,0)$ and $(-2,0)$

2) Which graph best represents $y = 8(0.75)^x$?

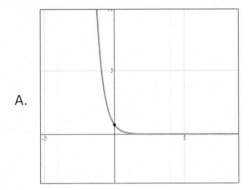   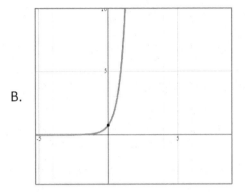

A.   B.

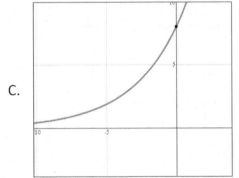   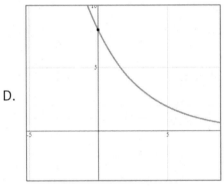

C.   D.

3) Which of the following is one solution to this equation?

$$x^2 + 2x - 5 = 0$$

A. $\sqrt{2} + 1$

B. $\sqrt{2} - 1$

C. $\sqrt{6} + 1$

D. $\sqrt{6} - 1$

4) Divide: $\frac{16n^6 - 32n^2 + 8n}{8n}$.

A. $2n^5 - 4n$

B. $2n^6 - 4n^2$

C. $2n^5 - 4n + 1$

D. $2n^6 - 4n^2 + 1$

$$4x^2 + 6x - 3, 3x^2 - 5x + 8$$

5) Which of the following is the sum of the two polynomials shown above?

A. $x^2 + 5x + 4$

B. $4x^2 - 6x + 3$

C. $5x^2 + 3x + 4$

D. $7x^2 + x + 5$

6) The table represents some points on the graph of linear function f.

x	-1	0	3	4	7
$f(x)$	-48	-36	0	12	48

Which function represents f?

A. $y = -12(x - 3)$

B. $y = 2(12x - 1)$

C. $y = -7(x - 4)$

D. $y = 12(x - 3)$

7) The graph of the quadratic function is shown on the grid.

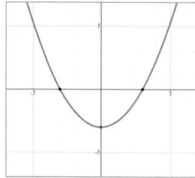

Which function is best represented by this graph?

A. $y = -3x^2 - 3$

B. $y = -\frac{1}{3}x^2 - 3$

C. $y = \frac{1}{3}x^2 - 3$

D. $y = 3x^2 + 3$

8) The graph of $f(x) = x^2$ was translated as 1 unit to the left and 2 units up to create the graph of function n. Which function represents n?

   A. $n(x) = (x + 1)^2 - 2$

   B. $n(x) = (x - 1)^2 - 2$

   C. $n(x) = (x + 1)^2 + 2$

   D. $n(x) = (x - 1)^2 + 2$

9) The amount of water in an artificial lake decreases by 0.06% per day. The amount of water in the lake was initially 450,000 cubic meters. Which function models the amount of water in cubic meters remaining after a week?

   A. $f(w) = 1.03(450,000)^w$

   B. $f(w) = 450,000(0.93)^w$

   C. $f(w) = 450,000(1.03)^w$

   D. $f(w) = 0.93(450,000)^w$

10) Which expression is a factor of $15x^2 - 12x - 3$?

   A. $x + 1$

   B. $5x + 1$

   C. $5x - 1$

   D. $3x - 1$

11) Which inequality is best represented by the graph?

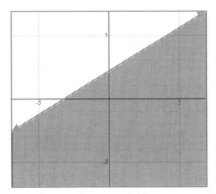

   A. $3y + 2x < 2$

   B. $3y + 2x \geq 2$

   C. $3y - 2x \leq 2$

   D. $3y - 2x > 2$

12) Which graph best represents $p(x) = (x - 2)(x + 3)$?

A.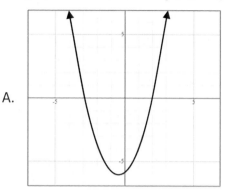

B.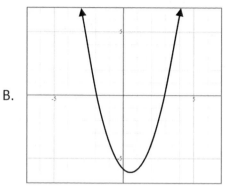

C.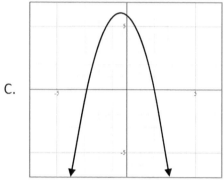

D.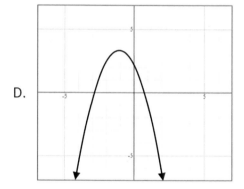

13) If $x \neq 0$ and $x = x^{-6}$, what is the value of x?

A. 1

B. 2

C. -2

D. 3

14) Which of the following is the equation of a quadratic graph with a vertex $(3, -3)$?

A. $y = 3x^2 - 3$

B. $y = -3x^2 + 3$

C. $y = x^2 + 3x - 3$

D. $y = 4(x - 3)^2 - 3$

15) Which of the following is equal to $m^{\frac{1}{2}} n^{-2} m^4 n^{\frac{2}{3}}$?

A. $m^2 n^{-\frac{4}{3}}$

B. $\dfrac{1}{m^{\frac{9}{4}} n^{\frac{4}{3}}}$

C. $\dfrac{m^{\frac{9}{4}}}{n^{\frac{4}{3}}}$

D. $\dfrac{m^{\frac{9}{2}}}{n^{\frac{4}{3}}}$

16) An editor earns \$400 per week for working 30 hours plus \$15 per hour worked over 30 hours. She can work a maximum of 54 hours per week.

Which graph best represents the editor's weekly earnings in dollars for working h hours over 30?

A.

B.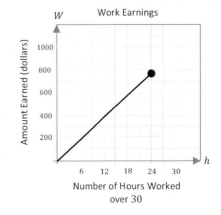

C.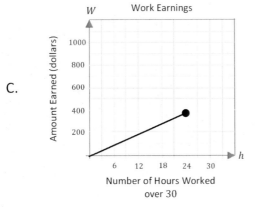

D.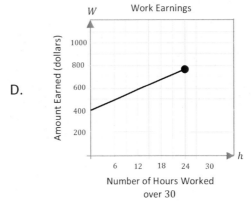

17) Which graph best represents a function with a range of all real numbers less than or equal to -1?

A.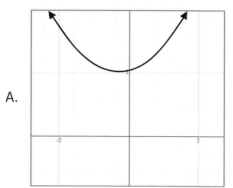

B.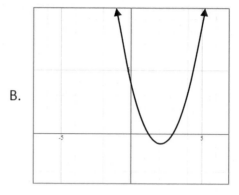

C.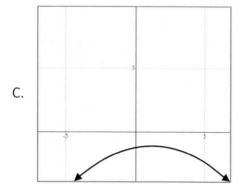

D.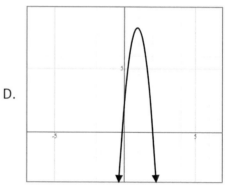

18) Which of the following is equal to the expression below?

$$\frac{8}{\sqrt{5} - 1}$$

A. $\sqrt{5} + 1$

B. $2(\sqrt{5} + 1)$

C. 1

D. $\sqrt{5}$

19) The conversion of degrees to degrees Celsius can be represented by a linear relationship. The graph shows the linear relationship between y, the temperature in degrees Celsius, and x, the temperature in degrees Fahrenheit from the freezing point of water.
Which equation best represents this situation?

A. $y = \frac{5}{9}x$

B. $y = \frac{9}{5} + 32$

C. $y = \frac{5}{9}(x - 32)$

D. $y = \frac{9}{5}(x - 32)$

20) A football team had $20,000 to spend on supplies. The team spent $14,000 on new balls. New sports shoes cost $120 each. Which of the following inequalities represents the number of new shoes the team can purchase?

A. $120x - 14{,}000 \le 20{,}000$

B. $120x + 14{,}000 \le 20{,}000$

C. $120x + 14{,}000 \ge 20{,}000$

D. $14{,}000x + 120 \le 20{,}000$

21) Jack earns $616 for his first 44 hours of work in a week and is then paid 1.5 times his regular hourly rate for any additional hours. This week, Jack needs $826 to pay his rent, bills, and other expenses. How many hours must he work to make enough money this week?

A. 54

B. 43

C. 48

D. 52

22) Which expression is equivalent to $35r^2 - 28r$?

A. $7r(5r - 4)$

B. $7r(5r + 4)$

C. $7(5r + 4)$

D. $7(5r - 4)$

23) A rocket is launched into the air from the ground. The table shows the height of the rocket, $h(x)$ at different times.

Time (seconds)	Height (meters)
5	748
10	1289
15	1621
20	1743
25	1651
30	1351
35	839

Based on the table, which function can best be used to model this situation?

A. $y = 12t^2 + 374$

B. $y = -4.2t^2 + 171t$

C. $y = -4.2t^2 + 165t - 30$

D. $y = 12t^2 - 218t + 1742$

STOP
This is the End of this Section.

Keystone Algebra I Practice Test 3

2024

Part 2

Total number of questions: 4

Total time: No time limit

You may use a calculator on this part.

47

24) The expression $6x^2 + 4x - 10$ can be written in factored form as $(2x - m)(3x + 5)$, where m represents a number. What is the value of m?

25) What is the negative solution to the equation $0 = \frac{2x^2}{5} - 10$?

26) Given $f(x^3) = 2x - 5$, for all values of x, what is the value of $f(8)$?

27) What is the positive value of x in solution set of this equation? $2 = \frac{3x}{2-x} - x$

End of Keystone Algebra I Practice Test 3

Keystone Algebra I Practice Test 4

2024

Two Parts

Total number of questions: 27

Part 1: 23 questions

Part 2: 4 questions

Total time: No time limit

51

Keystone Algebra I Practice Test Answer Sheet

Remove (or photocopy) this answer sheet and use it to complete the practice test.

Keystone Algebra I Practice Test 4 Answer Sheet

1	Ⓐ Ⓑ Ⓒ Ⓓ	21	Ⓐ Ⓑ Ⓒ Ⓓ
2	Ⓐ Ⓑ Ⓒ Ⓓ	22	Ⓐ Ⓑ Ⓒ Ⓓ
3	Ⓐ Ⓑ Ⓒ Ⓓ	23	Ⓐ Ⓑ Ⓒ Ⓓ
4	Ⓐ Ⓑ Ⓒ Ⓓ	24	
5	Ⓐ Ⓑ Ⓒ Ⓓ	25	
6	Ⓐ Ⓑ Ⓒ Ⓓ	26	
7	Ⓐ Ⓑ Ⓒ Ⓓ	27	
8	Ⓐ Ⓑ Ⓒ Ⓓ		
9	Ⓐ Ⓑ Ⓒ Ⓓ		
10	Ⓐ Ⓑ Ⓒ Ⓓ		
11	Ⓐ Ⓑ Ⓒ Ⓓ		
12	Ⓐ Ⓑ Ⓒ Ⓓ		
13	Ⓐ Ⓑ Ⓒ Ⓓ		
14	Ⓐ Ⓑ Ⓒ Ⓓ		
15	Ⓐ Ⓑ Ⓒ Ⓓ		
16	Ⓐ Ⓑ Ⓒ Ⓓ		
17	Ⓐ Ⓑ Ⓒ Ⓓ		
18	Ⓐ Ⓑ Ⓒ Ⓓ		
19	Ⓐ Ⓑ Ⓒ Ⓓ		
20	Ⓐ Ⓑ Ⓒ Ⓓ		

Keystone Algebra I Practice Test 4

2024

Part 1

Total number of questions: 23

Total time: No time limit

You may use a calculator on this part.

53

1) The graph of quadratic function f was transformed to create the graph of $g(x) = f(x + 3) + 2$.

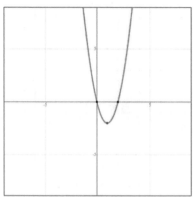

Which graph best represents g?

A.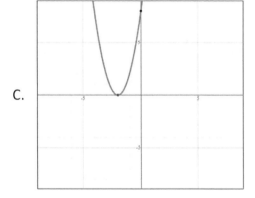

B.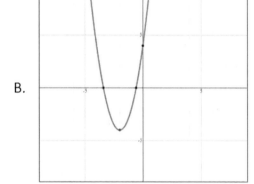

C.

D.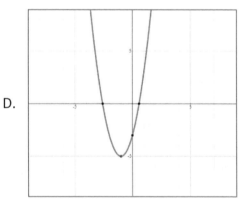

2) Which of the following is a factor of $6x^2 - 4x - 10$?

A. $x - 1$

B. $3x - 2$

C. $3x - 5$

D. $4x - 2$

3) The table shows the heights and the lengths of several rectangles.

Height (cm)	36	70	16	30	10	87	53	28	9	39
Length (cm)	21	20	32	11	18	45	38	23	42	39

What does the correlation coefficient for the data indicate about the strength of the linear association between the height and the length of these rectangles?

A. Weak positive correction

B. Weak negative correction

C. Strong negative correction

D. Strong positive correction

4) The graph of an exponential function is shown on the grid.

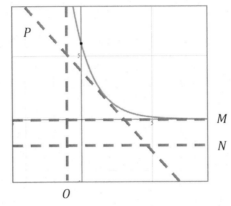

Which dashed line is an asymptote for the graph?

A. Line M

B. Line N

C. Line O

D. Line P

5) The graph of $f(x) = x^2$ was transformed to create the graph of $g(x) = f\left(-\frac{x}{2}\right) - 4$.

Which of the following statements is true about the graphs of f and g?

A. The graph of g is a reflection of the graph of f across the $x-$axis.

B. The vertex of the graph of g is 4 units to the right of the vertex of the graph of f.

C. The graph of g is a reflection of the graph of f across the $y-$axis.

D. The $y-$intercept of the graph of g is 4 units above the $y-$intercept of the graph of f.

6) Which of the following is equal to x^{yz} for all values of $x, y,$ and z?

    A. $x^{(y+z)}$

    B. $x^y z$

    C. $x^y x^z$

    D. $(x^y)^z$

7) Simplify $-15a(a + b)^2 + 23a(a + b)^2 =.$

    A. $8a(a + b)^2$

    B. $8a$

    C. $8(a + b)$

    D. $8(a + b)^2$

8) Which graph best represents the solution set of $y > -3x$?

A.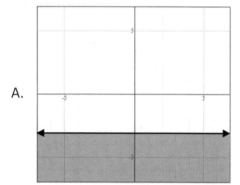

B.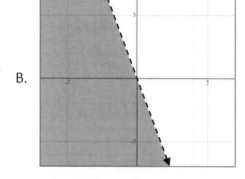

C.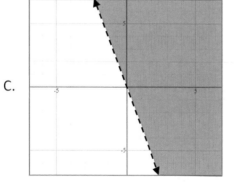

D.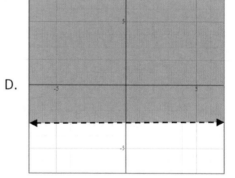

9) Which statement about the graph of $f(x) = 4(1.25)^x$ is true?
   A. The graph includes the point $(-1,2)$.

   B. There is an asymptote to the equation of $x = 0$.

   C. The x −intercept is 4.

   D. It is an increasing function.

10) The graph of a function is shown on the grid.

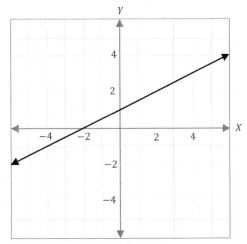

Which ordered pair best represents the location of the y −intercept?

A. $(0,1)$

B. $(-2,0)$

C. $(0,-2)$

D. $(1,0)$

11) The graph below represents part of an exponential function.
    Which statement is best supported by the graph?

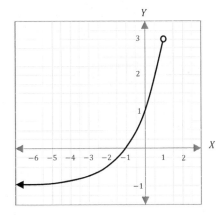

A. The y −intercept is -1.

B. The domain of the function is $(-\infty, 1]$.

C. The range of the function is $(-1,3)$.

D. The x −intercept is 1.

12) If $f(x^2) = 3x + 4$, for all positive values of x, what is the value of $f(121)$?

   A. 29

   B. -29

   C. -33

   D. 37

13) If a and b are solutions of the following equation, which of the following is the ratio $\frac{a}{b}$?

   $(a > b)$ $\qquad\qquad\qquad 2x^2 - 11x + 8 = -3x + 18$

   A. $\frac{1}{5}$

   B. $-\frac{1}{5}$

   C. 5

   D. -5

14) What is the parent graph of the following function and what transformations have taken place on it? $y = x^2 - 2$

   A. The parent graph is $y = x^2$, which is shifted 2 units up.

   B. The parent graph is $y = x^2$, which is shifted 2 units down.

   C. The parent graph is $y = x^2$, which is shifted 2 units left.

   D. The parent graph is $y = x^2$, which is shifted 2 units right.

15) Which of the following is the expansion of $(3x + 2)^3$?

   A. $27x^3 + 54x^2 + 36x + 8$

   B. $3x^3 + 18x^2 + 18x + 8$

   C. $3x^3 + 12x^2 + 18x + 8$

   D. $27x^3 + 18x^2 + 12x + 8$

16) If a quadratic function with equation $y = ax^2 + 5x + 10$, where a is constant, passes through the point $(2, 12)$, what is the value of a^2?

   A. 2

   B. -2

   C. 4

   D. -4

17) A graph of a quadratic function is shown on the grid.

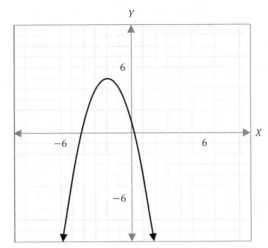

Which coordinates best represent the vertex of the graph?

A. $(0,1)$

B. $(-2,5)$

C. $(0.2,0)$

D. $(-4.2,0)$

18) Which function is equivalent to $f(x) = 2(2 - 3x)^2 - 7$?

A. $f(x) = 18x^2 - 24x + 1$

B. $f(x) = 18x^2 + 1$

C. $f(x) = -18x^2 - 24x + 1$

D. $f(x) = 18x^2 + 24x + 1$

19) What is the solution to the following system of equations? $\begin{cases} \dfrac{-x}{2} + \dfrac{y}{4} = 1 \\ \dfrac{-5y}{6} + 2x = 4 \end{cases}$

A. $x = 20, y = 50$

B. $x = 20, y = 48$

C. $x = 22, y = 48$

D. $x = 48, y = 22$

20) If $8 + 2x$ is 16 more than 20, what is the value of $6x$?

    A. 40

    B. 55

    C. 62

    D. 84

21) Which graph corresponds to the following inequalities?

$$y \leq x + 4$$
$$2x + y \leq -4$$

A.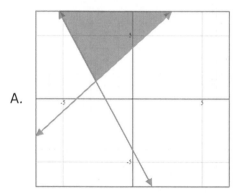

B.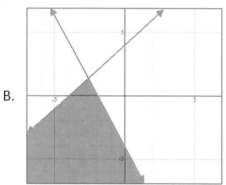

C.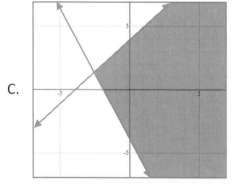

D.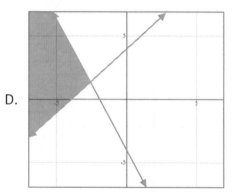

22) Which statement about $p(x) = 4x^2 - 81$ is true?

    A. The factors of p are $(x - 4.5)$ and $(x - 4.5)$.

    B. The factors of p are $(x + 9)$ and $(x - 4.5)$.

    C. The factors of p are $(x - 4.5)$ and $(x - 9)$.

    D. The factors of p are $(x + 4.5)$ and $(x - 4.5)$.

23) Which of the following points lies on line $2x + 4y = 6$?

    A. $(2, 1)$

    B. $(-1, 2)$

    C. $(-2, 2)$

    D. $(2, 2)$

STOP

This is the End of this Section.

Keystone Algebra I Practice Test 4

2024

Part 2

Total number of questions: 4

Total time: No time limit

You may use a calculator on this part.

63

24) The table shows the linear relationship between the distance in feet above the ground level and the time in seconds traveled by a dirigible.
What is the rate of change of the distance in feet above the ground level with respect to the time that the dirigible traveled?

Dirigible

Time (seconds)	Distance Below See Level (feet)
0	72
14	198
27	315
49	513
91	891
103	999
146	1,386

25) The graph of linear function g is shown on the grid.

What is the zero of g?

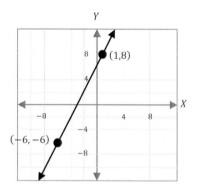

26) The value of a is directly proportional to the value of b. When $a = 2.5$, the value of b is 7.

What is the value of b when $a = 15$?

27) The graph of quadratic function f is shown on the grid. If $g(x) = x^2$ and $f(x) = g(x) + k$, what is the value of k?

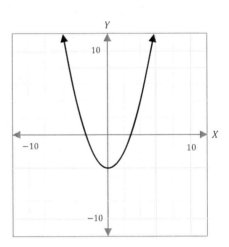

End of Keystone Algebra I Practice Test 4

Keystone Algebra I Practice Test 5

2024

Two Parts

Total number of questions: 27

Part 1: 23 questions

Part 2: 4 questions

Total time: No time limit

67

Keystone Algebra I Practice Test Answer Sheet

Remove (or photocopy) this answer sheet and use it to complete the practice test.

Keystone Algebra I Practice Test 5 Answer Sheet

1	Ⓐ Ⓑ Ⓒ Ⓓ	21	Ⓐ Ⓑ Ⓒ Ⓓ
2	Ⓐ Ⓑ Ⓒ Ⓓ	22	Ⓐ Ⓑ Ⓒ Ⓓ
3	Ⓐ Ⓑ Ⓒ Ⓓ	23	Ⓐ Ⓑ Ⓒ Ⓓ
4	Ⓐ Ⓑ Ⓒ Ⓓ	24	
5	Ⓐ Ⓑ Ⓒ Ⓓ	25	
6	Ⓐ Ⓑ Ⓒ Ⓓ	26	
7	Ⓐ Ⓑ Ⓒ Ⓓ	27	
8	Ⓐ Ⓑ Ⓒ Ⓓ		
9	Ⓐ Ⓑ Ⓒ Ⓓ		
10	Ⓐ Ⓑ Ⓒ Ⓓ		
11	Ⓐ Ⓑ Ⓒ Ⓓ		
12	Ⓐ Ⓑ Ⓒ Ⓓ		
13	Ⓐ Ⓑ Ⓒ Ⓓ		
14	Ⓐ Ⓑ Ⓒ Ⓓ		
15	Ⓐ Ⓑ Ⓒ Ⓓ		
16	Ⓐ Ⓑ Ⓒ Ⓓ		
17	Ⓐ Ⓑ Ⓒ Ⓓ		
18	Ⓐ Ⓑ Ⓒ Ⓓ		
19	Ⓐ Ⓑ Ⓒ Ⓓ		
20	Ⓐ Ⓑ Ⓒ Ⓓ		

Keystone Algebra I Practice Test 5

2024

Part 1

Total number of questions: 13

Total time: No time limit

You may use a calculator on this part.

69

1) Which of the following is equivalent to $\sqrt[3]{324}$?

   A. $3\sqrt[3]{12}$

   B. $2\sqrt{81}$

   C. $12\sqrt[3]{3}$

   D. 18

2) $(x^6)^{\frac{7}{8}}$ is equal to ...

   A. $x^{\frac{19}{4}}$

   B. $x^{\frac{21}{4}}$

   C. $x^{\frac{23}{4}}$

   D. $x^{\frac{25}{4}}$

3) A sequence can be generated by using $a_n = 3a_{n-1} - a_{n-2}$, where $a_1 = 3$, $a_2 = 2$, and n is a whole number greater than 1. What are the first five terms in the sequence?

   A. $3, 2, 1, 0, -1$

   B. $3, 2, 3, 7, 18$

   C. $3, 2, 6, 4, 18$

   D. $3, 2, 4, 1, 5$

4) Which of the following expressions is equivalent to $2x(5 + 3y + 2x + 4z)$?

   A. $7x + 5xy + 4x + 6xz$

   B. $5x + 3xy + 4x^2 + 4xz$

   C. $6xy + 4x^2 + 8xz + 10$

   D. $10x + 6xy + 4x^2 + 8xz$

5) The graph of quadratic parent function f was transformed to create the graph of $k(x) = f(x + 4) - 5$. Which graph best represents k?

A.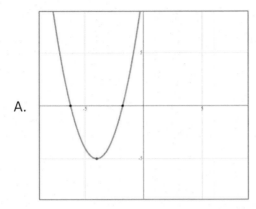

B.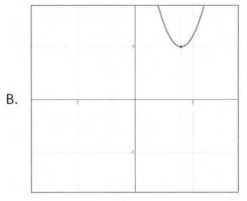

C.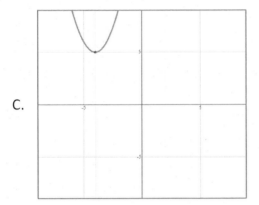

D.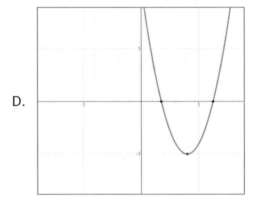

6) If Anna multiplies her age by 5 and then adds 3, she will get a number equal to her mother's age. If x is her mother's age, what is Anna's age in terms of x?

A. $\frac{x-3}{5}$

B. $\frac{x-5}{3}$

C. $\frac{x+5}{3}$

D. $3x + 5$

7) The population of buffaloes in the 18th century is modeled by an exponential function f, where x is the number of decades after the year 1850. The graph of f is shown on the grid. Which inequality best represents the range of f in this situation?

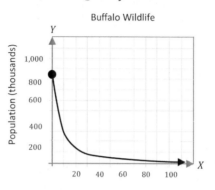

Buffalo Wildlife

Time After 1850 (decades)

A. $x > 0$

B. $y \leq 850$

C. $0 \leq x \leq 1,960$

D. $0 < y \leq 850$

8) Perform the operations and simplify $\sqrt{8} - \sqrt{50} + \sqrt{72}$.

A. $\sqrt{2}$

B. $3\sqrt{2}$

C. $-6\sqrt{2}$

D. $13\sqrt{2}$

9) Given $g(x) = x^2 - 2x - 15$, which statement is true?

A. The zeroes are 3 and 5 because the factors of g are $(x + 3)$ and $(x + 5)$.

B. The zeroes are -3 and 5 because the factors of g are $(x - 3)$ and $(x + 5)$.

C. The zeroes are -3 and 5 because the factors of g are $(x + 3)$ and $(x - 5)$.

D. The zeroes are 3 and 5 because the factors of g are $(x - 3)$ and $(x - 5)$.

10) Which of the following Lines is parallel to $6y - 2x = 24$?

A. $y = x - 2$

B. $y = -x - 1$

C. $y = \frac{1}{3}x + 2$

D. $y = 2x - 1$

11) If $4n - 3 \geq 1$, what is the least possible value of $4n + 3$?

   A. 3

   B. 4

   C. 7

   D. 9

12) The graph shows the height in feet of a stone ball above the ground t seconds after it was launched from the ground.

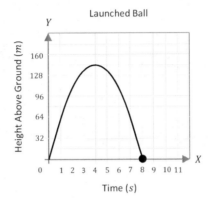

Launched Ball

Which function is best represented by the graph of this situation?
A. $y = -9t^2 - 72t$
B. $y = -9t^2 - 144t - 576$
C. $y = -9t^2 + 72t$
D. $y = -9t^2 + 144t - 576$

13) If $(x - 2)^3 = 27$ which of the following could be the value of $(x - 6)(x - 4)$?

   A. 1

   B. -1

   C. 3

   D. -3

14) Which expression is equivalent $-49x^2 + 9$?

   A. $(7x + 3)(7x - 3)$

   B. $(7x + 3)(7x + 3)$

   C. $(-7x + 3)(7x - 3)$

   D. $(7x + 3)(-7x + 3)$

15) What is the slope of the shown line?

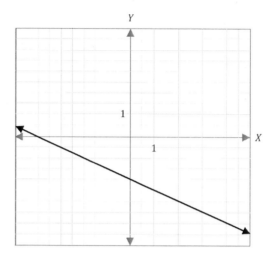

    A. 1

    B. -1

    C. -2

    D. $-\frac{1}{2}$

16) Find the $y-$intercepts and $x-$intercepts: $3x - 6y = 24$.

    A. $\begin{cases} (0,4) \\ (8,0) \end{cases}$

    B. $\begin{cases} (0,-4) \\ (8,0) \end{cases}$

    C. $\begin{cases} (0,4) \\ (-8,0) \end{cases}$

    D. $\begin{cases} (0,4) \\ (-8,0) \end{cases}$

17) What are the zeros of the function: $f(x) = x^2 - 7x + 12$?

    A. 0

    B. 4, 3

    C. $-4, -3$

    D. $-2, -3$

18) The cost of using a car is $0.35 per minute. Which of the following equations represents the total cost c, in dollars, for h hours of using the car?

A. $c = \frac{60h}{035}$

B. $c = \frac{0.35}{60h}$

C. $c = 0.35(60h)$

D. $c = 60h + 0.35$

19) For what value of x is the function $f(x)$ below undefined?
$$f(x) = \frac{1}{(x-3)^2 + 4(x-3) + 4}$$

A. 1

B. -1

C. 1.5

D. 2

20) How long will it take to receive $360 in the investment of $240 at the rate of 10% simple interest?

A. 9 years

B. 15 years

C. 16 years

D. 18 years

21) Five years ago, Amy was three times as old as Mike was. If Mike is 10 years old now, how old is Amy?

A. 4

B. 8

C. 12

D. 20

22) The graph of quadratic function f is shown on
the grid.
Which of these best represents the domain of
f?
A. $-6 \leq x \leq -1$
B. $y \leq 5$
C. All real numbers
D. All real numbers less than 5

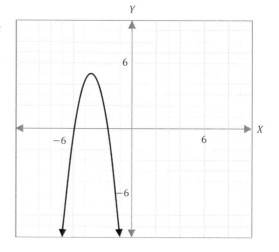

23) Which graph best represents the solution set of $x \leq 1$?

A.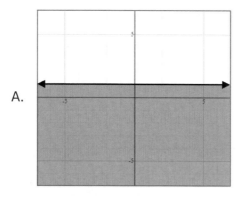

B.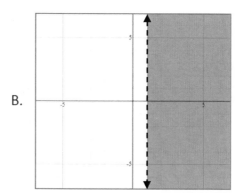

C.

D.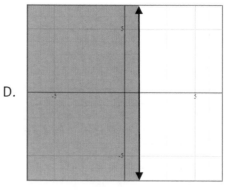

STOP
This is the End of this Section.

Keystone Algebra I Practice Test 5

2024

Part 2

Total number of questions: 4

Total time: No time limit

You may use a calculator on this part.

77

24) What is the value of the y −intercept of the graph of $k(x) = 42 \left(\frac{4}{5}\right)^x$?

25) Solve for x in this equation. $-(6x - 7) = 5(8 + x)$

26) The expression $(xy^{-2})^3 \left(\frac{y}{x}\right)^9$ is equivalent to $x^n y^m$ is the value of $n - m$?

27) The value of y is directly proportional to the value of x. If $y = 4$ when $x = 7$, what is the value of y when $x = 17.5$?

End of Keystone Algebra I Practice Test 5

Keystone Algebra I Practice Test 6

2024

Two Parts

Total number of questions: 27

Part 1: 23 questions

Part 2: 4 questions

Total time: No time limit

81

Keystone Algebra I Practice Test Answer Sheet

Remove (or photocopy) this answer sheet and use it to complete the practice test.

Keystone Algebra I Practice Test 6 Answer Sheet

1	(A) (B) (C) (D)	21	(A) (B) (C) (D)
2	(A) (B) (C) (D)	22	(A) (B) (C) (D)
3	(A) (B) (C) (D)	23	(A) (B) (C) (D)
4	(A) (B) (C) (D)	24	
5	(A) (B) (C) (D)	25	
6	(A) (B) (C) (D)	26	
7	(A) (B) (C) (D)	27	
8	(A) (B) (C) (D)		
9	(A) (B) (C) (D)		
10	(A) (B) (C) (D)		
11	(A) (B) (C) (D)		
12	(A) (B) (C) (D)		
13	(A) (B) (C) (D)		
14	(A) (B) (C) (D)		
15	(A) (B) (C) (D)		
16	(A) (B) (C) (D)		
17	(A) (B) (C) (D)		
18	(A) (B) (C) (D)		
19	(A) (B) (C) (D)		
20	(A) (B) (C) (D)		

Keystone Algebra I Practice Test 6

2024

Part 1

Total number of questions: 23

Total time: No time limit

You may use a calculator on this part.

83

1) The late fee for overdue books at a library is $0.2 per day per book, with a maximum late fee of $4.00 per book. Which graph models the total late fee for 5 books that were checked out on the same day and are overdue?

A.

Fees for Overdue Books

B.

Fees for Overdue Books

C.

Feed for Overdue Books

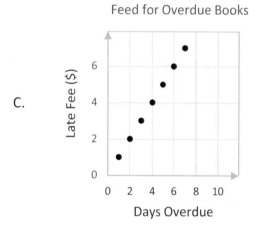

D.

Fee for Overdue Books

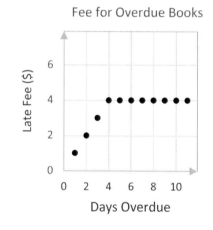

2) The following equation expresses the approximate height h, in feet, of a discus t seconds after it is launched vertically upward from the ground with an initial velocity of 44 feet per second. After approximately how many seconds will the discus hit the ground ? $h = -10t^2 + 44t$

A. 2.9

B. 4.4

C. 5.9

D. 8.0

3) If $y = -\frac{3}{4}x - 1$, what is the value of x when $y = -6$?

 A. $-\frac{20}{3}$

 B. $\frac{7}{2}$

 C. $\frac{20}{3}$

 D. $-\frac{7}{2}$

4) The set of ordered pairs below represents some points on the graph of function f.

$$\{(2,5)(0,1)(4,17)(-1,-1)(-3,1)\}$$

 What is the parent function of f?

 A. $y = x$

 B. $y = 2^x$

 C. $y = x^2$

 D. $y = \sqrt{x}$

5) If $y = 3x^2 + 6x + 2$ is graphed in the xy −plane, which of the following characteristics of the graph is displayed as a constant or coefficient in the equation?

 A. y −coordinate of the vertex

 B. x −intercept(s)

 C. y −intercept

 D. x −intercept of the symmetry

6) What are the x −intercepts of the graph of the quadratic function $h(x) = -2x^2 + 2x + 4$?

 A. $(-1,2)$ and $(2,0)$

 B. $(-1,0)$ and $(2,0)$

 C. $(-1,2)$ and $(0,-2)$

 D. $(1,0)$ and $(2,0)$

7) For the function f, $f(-6) = 12$ and $f(12) = 6$. If $y = f(x)$, what is the value of y when $x = 12$?

 A. $y = -6$

 B. $y = 6$

 C. $y = 12$

 D. $y = -12$

8) The lift at a construction site is loaded with the same number of blocks every time it is used. The table below shows the total number of blocks carried as a function of the number of times the lift is used.

Construction Site Lift

Number of Times Used	Total Number of Blocks Carried
4	360
8	720
12	1,080
16	1,440

Based on the data in the table, what is the total number of blocks that will have been carried when the lift is used 11 times?

A. 40

B. 360

C. 90

D. 990

9) What is the zero of the linear function graphed below?

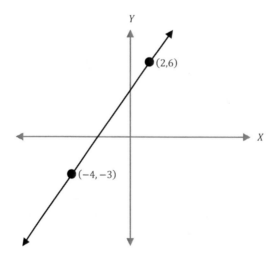

A. 2

B. 3

C. −3

D. −2

10) A store ordered 50 crates of apples for the fall season. The total number of apples can be determined using the function $f(x) = 150x + 25$, where x represents the number of crates ordered. However, due to a storm, some of the apples were damaged and the store had to throw them away. If the function to model the situation is changed to $g(x) = 135x + 25$, how many fewer apples will the store have available if they still order 50 crates?

A. 7525

B. 50

C. 6775

D. 750

11) The graph of quadratic function q is shown on the grid.

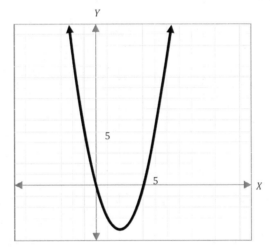

What is a solution to $q(x) = 5$?

A. 4

B. 0

C. 1

D. 5

12) The population of the city is currently 12,000. The function $p = 12,000 + 10t^2$ can be used to estimate p, the population of the city t years from now. Based on this function, which statement is true?

A. The population of the city is increasing at a constant rate.

B. The population of the city will reach 15,000 between 17 and 18 years from now.

C. The population of the city will increase by 200 people two years from now.

D. The population of the city will increase and then decrease.

13) The mapping below represents y as a quadratic function of x.

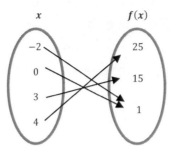

Which representation shows the same relationship between x and y?

A.

x	$f(x)$
−2	1
0	0
2	9
4	25

C.

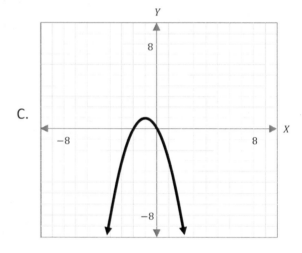

B. $g(x) = x^2 + 2x - 3$

D. $\{(-2,1), (0,1), (3,15), (4,25)\}$

14) What is the equation in the standard form of the line that passes through the point $(2,15)$ and has a slope of 1.5?

A. $2x - 3y = 9$
B. $3x + 2y = 24$
C. $3x - 2y = -24$
D. $3x + 2y = 9$

15) What is the vertex of the graph of the quadratic function $g(x) = 3x^2 + 4x + 2$?

A. $\left(-\frac{2}{3}, \frac{4}{3}\right)$
B. $\left(-\frac{2}{3}, \frac{2}{3}\right)$
C. $\left(-\frac{4}{3}, \frac{4}{3}\right)$
D. $\left(-\frac{4}{3}, \frac{2}{3}\right)$

16) The table represents different values of function $g(x)$.

What is the value of $1 - g\big(g(-2)\big) + 2g(0)$?

x	-2	-1	0	1	4
$g(x)$	4	-2	1	0	3

A. -2

B. 1

C. 0

D. 3

17) The graph of line f is shown on the grid.

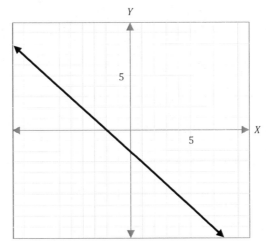

Line g is less steep than line f and has a $y-$intercept that is above the $y-$intercept of line f. Which function could be represented by line g?

A. $y = \frac{5}{3}x - 3$

B. $y = \frac{3}{5}x + 3$

C. $y = \frac{3}{5}x - 3$

D. $y = \frac{5}{3}x + 3$

18) Which expression is equivalent to $-5x^2 - 9x + 2$?

A. $(-5x + 1)(x - 2)$

B. $(5x - 2)(-x + 1)$

C. $(5x + 2)(-x - 1)$

D. $(-5x + 1)(x + 2)$

19) Function k has a parent function. The table shows some ordered pairs that belong to k.

x	$k(x)$
-2	-10
-1	-1
0	4
2	2
4	-16

Which graph shows the parent function of k?

A.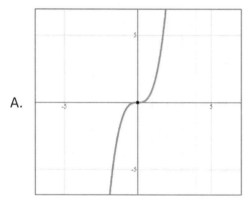

B.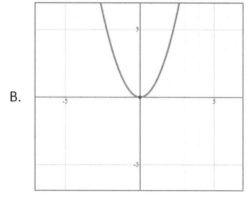

C.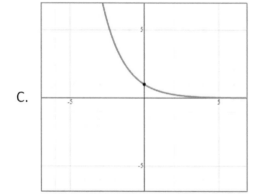

D.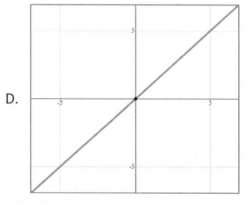

20) A painter charges $40 per hour for labor plus $60 for a ladder rental when he paints a house. The customer provides the paint. The total charge to paint a customer's house was $1,100. How many hours did the painter spend painting this house?

A. $20h$

B. $25h$

C. $30h$

D. Not here

21) What is the range of the function graphed on the grid?

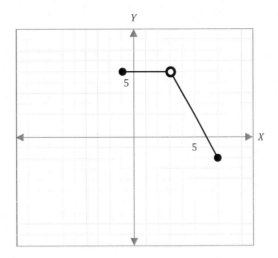

A. $\{y| - 2 \leq y \leq 6\}$
B. $\{x| - 1 \leq x \leq 7\}$
C. $\{y| - 2 \leq y < 6\}$
D. $\{x| - 1 \leq x < 3, 3 < x \leq 7\}$

22) The junior class needs a combined total of 300 small and large backpacks for their trip. The number of small backpacks needed is twice the number of large backpacks needed. Based on this information, would it be reasonable for the junior class to order 100 large backpacks and 200 small backpacks?

A. No, because the number of small backpacks is not twice the number of large backpacks.

B. No, because the number of large backpacks is not twice the number of small backpacks.

C. Yes, because the total number of backpacks is 300.

D. Yes, because the number of small backpacks is twice the number of large backpacks.

$$3x + x + x - 2 = x + x + x + 8$$

23) In the equation above, what is the value of x?

A. 3

B. 2

C. 5

D. 10

STOP
This is the End of this Section.

Keystone Algebra I Practice Test 6

2024

Part 2

Total number of questions: 4

Total time: No time limit

You may use a calculator on this part.

93

24) In the graph, a line in the xy −plan passes through the point $(2,2)$ and crosses the y −axis at the point $(0,4)$. The line crosses the x −axis at the point $(m, 0)$. What is the value of m?

25) For what real value of x is the equation below true?
$$x^3 - 6x^2 + 3x - 18 = 0$$

26) A construction worker can complete building a brick wall in 5 hours and a wooden fence in 3 hours. The function below can be used to find the number of brick walls the worker builds when she completes f wooden fences in a 40-hour workweek.
$$b = \frac{(50 - 3f)}{0.5}$$
If the worker built 10 brick walls in one week, how many wooden fences did she complete that week?

27) In the xy −plane, the equations $x + 3y = 7$ and $2x + 6y = a$ represent the same line for some constant a. What is the value of a?

End of Keystone Algebra I Practice Test 6

Keystone Algebra I Practice Test 7

2024

Two Parts

Total number of questions: 27

Part 1: 23 questions

Part 2: 4 questions

Total time: No time limit

97

Keystone Algebra I Practice Test Answer Sheet

Remove (or photocopy) this answer sheet and use it to complete the practice test.

Keystone Algebra I Practice Test 7 Answer Sheet

1 Ⓐ Ⓑ Ⓒ Ⓓ		21 Ⓐ Ⓑ Ⓒ Ⓓ
2 Ⓐ Ⓑ Ⓒ Ⓓ		22 Ⓐ Ⓑ Ⓒ Ⓓ
3 Ⓐ Ⓑ Ⓒ Ⓓ		23 Ⓐ Ⓑ Ⓒ Ⓓ
4 Ⓐ Ⓑ Ⓒ Ⓓ		24
5 Ⓐ Ⓑ Ⓒ Ⓓ		25
6 Ⓐ Ⓑ Ⓒ Ⓓ		26
7 Ⓐ Ⓑ Ⓒ Ⓓ		27
8 Ⓐ Ⓑ Ⓒ Ⓓ		
9 Ⓐ Ⓑ Ⓒ Ⓓ		
10 Ⓐ Ⓑ Ⓒ Ⓓ		
11 Ⓐ Ⓑ Ⓒ Ⓓ		
12 Ⓐ Ⓑ Ⓒ Ⓓ		
13 Ⓐ Ⓑ Ⓒ Ⓓ		
14 Ⓐ Ⓑ Ⓒ Ⓓ		
15 Ⓐ Ⓑ Ⓒ Ⓓ		
16 Ⓐ Ⓑ Ⓒ Ⓓ		
17 Ⓐ Ⓑ Ⓒ Ⓓ		
18 Ⓐ Ⓑ Ⓒ Ⓓ		
19 Ⓐ Ⓑ Ⓒ Ⓓ		
20 Ⓐ Ⓑ Ⓒ Ⓓ		

Keystone Algebra I Practice Test 7

2024

Part 1

Total number of questions: 23

Total time: No time limit

You may use a calculator on this part.

99

1) Which graph can be obtained by translating the graph of $k(x) = 2x^2 - 4$ up 5 units?

A.

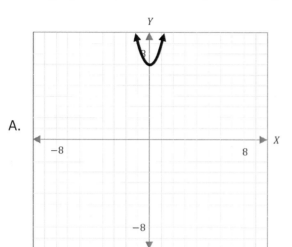

B.

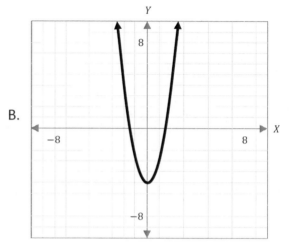

C.

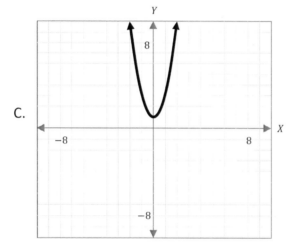

D.

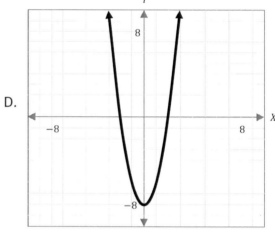

2) Which of the following is an equation of line t in the xy −plane below?

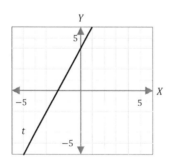

A. $4y - 2x = 2$

B. $4y - x = 2$

C. $y + 2x = 4$

D. $y - 2x = 4$

3) The graph shows the cost of purchasing x cookies at a candy shop if the cookies are equally priced.

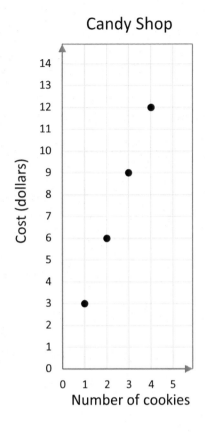

Candy Shop

Based on this information, which ordered pair represents an additional point on the graph?

A. $(5,15)$

B. $(7,20)$

C. $(10,30)$

D. $(6,18)$

4) The graph shows the time it takes for one worker to load 48 boxes into a truck.

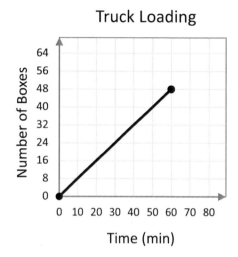

The next day two workers loaded twice the number of boxes in the same amount of time. If this new relationship is graphed on the same coordinate grid, which statement is true?

A. The new graph would have a $y-$intercept at 120.

B. The new graph would be steeper than the original graph.

C. The new graph would be less steep than the original graph.

D. The new graph would have a $y-$intercept at 96.

5) If $4x = \frac{48}{3}$, what is the value of 7^{x-2}?

A. 7

B. 14

C. 49

D. 343

6) Due to air pollution, an environmental engineer estimates that starting from the present, the population of a big city will decrease by 20 percent every 10 years. If the city's present population is 980,000, which of the following expressions represents the engineer's estimate of the population of the city t years from now?

A. $980,000(0.2)^{10t}$

B. $980,000(0.2)^{\frac{t}{10}}$

C. $980,000(0.8)^{10t}$

D. $980,000(0.8)^{\frac{t}{10}}$

7) At a rate of $3d + 9$ Kilometers per hour, how many kilometers can a train travel in 8 hours?

A. $7d + 27$

B. $12d + 36$

C. $18d + 48$

D. $24d + 72$

8) What is the zero of $r(x) = \frac{4}{7}x + 12$?

A. 21

B. -21

C. -12

D. 12

9) A customer pays an annual membership fee of $120 to a fitness center. Each time he goes to the gym, he pays only $6. The total amount of money he spends at the fitness center in one year in dollars can be found using the function $f(x) = 6x + 120$. What does the variable x represent in this function?

A. The total amount of money the customer spends each week at the fitness center.

B. The number of weeks the customer has been a member of the fitness center.

C. The number of times the customer goes to the gym in one year.

D. The cost each time the customer goes to the gym.

10) A television with a price of $300 is to be purchased with an initial payment of $60 and weekly payments of $30. Which of the following equations can be used to find the number of weekly payments, w, required to complete the purchase, assuming there are no taxes or fees?

A. $300 = 30w - 60$

B. $300 = 30w$

C. $300 = 30w + 60$

D. $300 = 60w - 30$

11) A landscaper needs to determine the amount of fertilizer he needs to buy to cover a circular lawn. If the lawn has a radius of r feet, and the landscaper always adds 10 square feet to the area to account for extra fertilizer, which function can be used to find the total area in square feet, $A(r)$, that the landscaper will use to determine how much fertilizer he needs to buy?

A. $A(r) = \pi r^2 + 10$

B. $A(r) = 2\pi r^2 + 10$

C. $A(r) = \pi(r + 10)^2$

D. $A(r) = \pi(r^2 + 10)$

12) The regular price for a concert ticket is $100. A different ticket vendor offers a 10% discount on the regular price. What would be the savings in dollars and cents if you purchase 3 tickets from the discounted vendor instead of the regular vendor?

A. $10

B. $100

C. $30

D. $90

13) The side lengths of the figure below are given in centimeters.

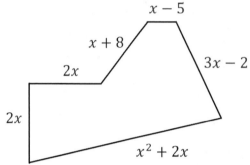

If the perimeter of this figure is 181 *cm*, what is the value of x?

A. -20

B. 9

C. -9

D. 20

14) What is the value of a in the solution to the following system of equations?

$$2a = 9 - 5b$$
$$3b = a - 6$$

A. $\frac{57}{11}$

B. -3

C. 11

D. $-\frac{11}{3}$

15) Function f is graphed below.

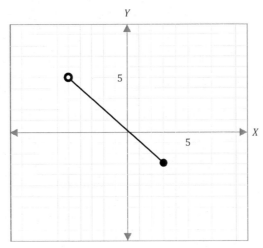

What is the range of f?
A. $\{y| -3 \leq y < 5\}$
B. $\{x| -5 < x \leq 3\}$
C. $\{x| -5 \leq x < 3\}$
D. $\{y| -3 < y \leq 5\}$

16) What is the vertex of the graph of the quadratic function $g(x) = 2x^2 - 4x + 5$?
A. $(1, -3)$
B. $(1, 3)$
C. $(2, -3)$
D. $(2, 5)$

17) The graph of $y = f(x)$ in the xy−plane is shown below. What is the value of $f(0)$?

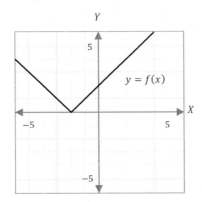

A. -2
B. -1
C. 0
D. 2

18) Which of the following equations represents a quadratic graph with a vertex at $(2, 5)$?

A. $y = 2x^2 + 5$

B. $y = -2x^2 + 5$

C. $y = x^2 + 2x + 5$

D. $y = 4(x - 2)^2 + 5$

19) A coffee shop charges $2.75 for a small coffee, $3.50 for a medium coffee, and $4.25 for a large coffee. Last week, the shop sold 90 medium coffees and 60 large coffees. If the total revenue from coffee sales was between $900 and $1000, which inequality represents the possible number of small coffees sold?

A. $110 \leq s \leq 130$

B. $100 \leq s \leq 130$

C. $110 \leq s \leq 140$

D. $100 \leq s \leq 140$

20) If the value of z varies inversely with w, which function represents the relationship between w and z if $z = 30$ when $w = 6$?

A. $z = \dfrac{180}{w}$

B. $z = \dfrac{5}{w}$

C. $z = \dfrac{w}{5}$

D. $z = \dfrac{w}{180}$

21) The scatterplot shows the number of free kicks that different football teams attempted and the number of goals from free kicks in a league.

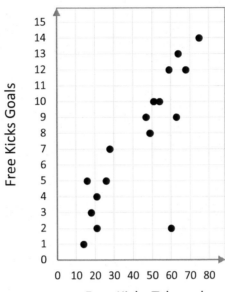

Free Kicks

Based on the trend in the data, approximately how many goals are scored from free kicks If 40 free kicks are taken during the season?

A. 4

B. 10

C. 14

D. 7

22) The slope and y −intercept of the line represented by $y = \frac{2}{3}x - \frac{8}{6}$ are both divided by $-\frac{1}{3}$ to create a new line. Which graph represents the new line?

A.
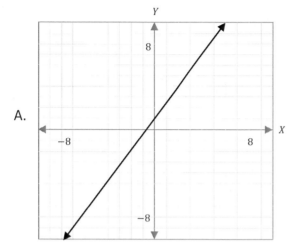

B.
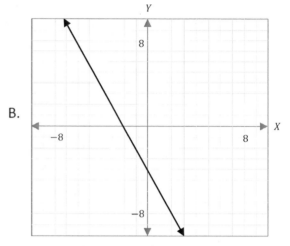

C.
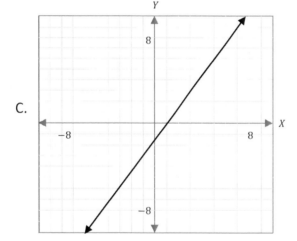

D.
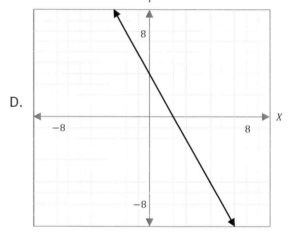

23) Which representation shows the same relationship as $h(x) = -\frac{1}{2}(3x + 11)$?

A.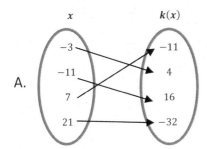

B.

x	$k(x)$
15	-28
12	-23.5
4	-11.5
-15	-17

C. $k = \{(-11,11), (-4,1), (6,-15), (17,-31), (19,-34)\}$

D.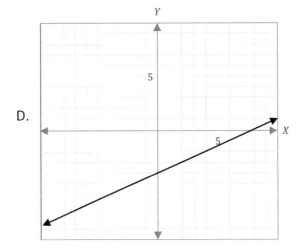

STOP
This is the End of this Section.

Keystone Algebra I Practice Test 7

2024

Part 2

Total number of questions: 4

Total time: No time limit

You may use a calculator on this part.

110

24) The sum of $-4x^2 + 3x - 24$ and $7x^2 - 8x + 18$ can be written in the form $ax^2 + bx + c$, where a, b, and c are constants. What is the value of $a + b - c$?

25) If $t > 0$ and $t^2 - 16 = 0$, what is the value of t?

26) The table below shows the number of international tourist arrivals, rounded to the nearest tenth of a million, to the top nine tourist destinations in both 2012 and 2013. The member of international tourist arrivals in Russia in 2012 was 13.5% greater than in 2011. The number of international tourist arrivals in Russia was k million more in 2012 than in 2011.

Country	2012	2013
France	83.0	84.7
United States	66.7	69.8
Spain	57.5	60.7
China	57.7	55.7
Italy	46.4	47.7
Turkey	35.7	37.8
Germany	30.4	31.5
United Kingdom	26.3	32.2
Russia	24.7	25.4

What is the value of k to the nearest integer?

27) The table shows the population, p, of ants in a field at the end of w weeks.

Dirigible

Time, w (weeks)	Population, p (in thousands)
0	2
1	6
2	18
3	54

Based on the data in the table, what will be the population of ants in the field at the end of 9 weeks?

End of Keystone Algebra 1 Practice Test 7

Keystone Algebra I Practice Test 8

2024

Two Parts

Total number of questions: 27

Part 1: 23 questions

Part 2: 4 questions

Total time: No time limit

113

Keystone Algebra I Practice Test Answer Sheet

Remove (or photocopy) this answer sheet and use it to complete the practice test.

Keystone Algebra I Practice Test 8 Answer Sheet		

1	(A)(B)(C)(D)	21	(A)(B)(C)(D)
2	(A)(B)(C)(D)	22	(A)(B)(C)(D)
3	(A)(B)(C)(D)	23	(A)(B)(C)(D)
4	(A)(B)(C)(D)	24	
5	(A)(B)(C)(D)	25	
6	(A)(B)(C)(D)	26	
7	(A)(B)(C)(D)	27	
8	(A)(B)(C)(D)		
9	(A)(B)(C)(D)		
10	(A)(B)(C)(D)		
11	(A)(B)(C)(D)		
12	(A)(B)(C)(D)		
13	(A)(B)(C)(D)		
14	(A)(B)(C)(D)		
15	(A)(B)(C)(D)		
16	(A)(B)(C)(D)		
17	(A)(B)(C)(D)		
18	(A)(B)(C)(D)		
19	(A)(B)(C)(D)		
20	(A)(B)(C)(D)		

Keystone Algebra I Practice Test 8

2024

Part 1

Total number of questions: 23

Total time: No time limit

You may use a calculator on this part.

115

1) Which value of x is the rational part of the solution to the equation $4x^2 - 9 = 12x$?

   A. $x = \frac{3}{2}$

   B. $x = -\frac{3}{2}$

   C. $x = 3$ and -3

   D. $x = -\frac{3}{2}$ and $x = \frac{3}{2}$

2) What is the solution to this equation?

$$5(x - 3) - 2(x + 5) = -13$$

   A. -3

   B. 2

   C. 3

   D. 4

3) Which inequality can be represented by the graph below?

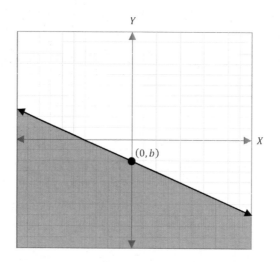

   A. $2y \leq -(x + b)$

   B. $x + 2y \leq 2b$

   C. $x - y \geq b$

   D. $2x - y \geq b$

4) Which expression is equivalent to $(2n - 5)(3n + 4)$?

   A. $6n^2 - 7n - 20$

   B. $6n^2 - n - 20$

   C. $5n^2 - 7n - 20$

   D. $5n^2 - n - 20$

5) Given $g(x) = x^2 - 49$, which statement is true?

   A. The only zero, 7, can be found when $0 = (x - 7)(x - 7)$.

   B. The only zero, 49, can be found when $0 = (x - 49)(x - 49)$.

   C. The zeros, -7 and 7, can be found when $0 = (x + 7)(x - 7)$.

   D. The zeros, -49 and 49, can be found when $0 = (x + 49)(x - 49)$.

6) What is the range of the function shown below?

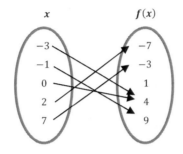

   A. $\{-3, -1, 0, 2, 7\}$

   B. $\{-7, -3, 1, 4, 9\}$

   C. $\{1\}$

   D. $\{-7, -3, 4, 9\}$

7) Which graph does not represent y as a function of x?

A.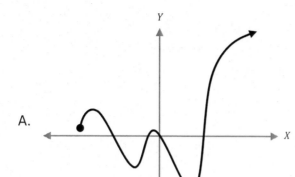

B.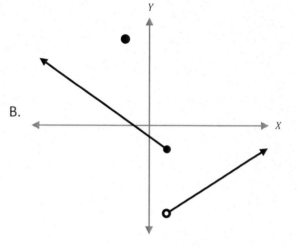

C.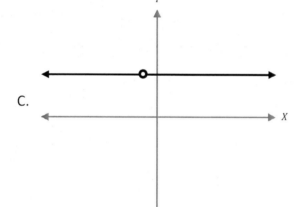

D.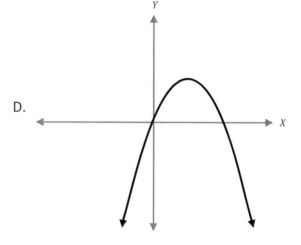

8) What is the positive solution to $2x^2 + 5x - 3 = 0$?

   A. $\frac{1}{2}$

   B. 3

   C. $\frac{1}{2}$ and 3

   D. 2 and 3

9) Which of the following graphs best represents a system of equations that has a solution in the fourth quadrant?

A.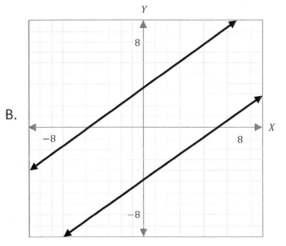

B.

C.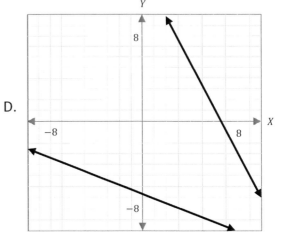

D.

10) Which table shows the same relationship as $y = 5x - 3x^2 + 2$?

A.

x	-2	-1	0	2	3
y	-20	-6	4	0	-1

B.

x	-2	-1	0	2	3
y	-20	-6	2	0	-10

C.

x	-2	-1	0	2	3
y	-20	4	2	0	-1

D.

x	-2	-1	0	2	3
y	-20	4	4	0	-10

11) The function $y = x^2 + 2x - 8$ is graphed below.

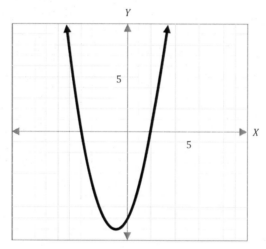

What are the values of x when $x^2 + 2x - 8 = -5$?

A. $x = -5$ and $x = 8$

B. $x = -4$ and $x = 2$

C. $x = -3$ and $x = 1$

D. $x = -3$ and $x = 2$

12) The slope and y −intercept of the graph of f were changed to make the graph of g, as shown below.

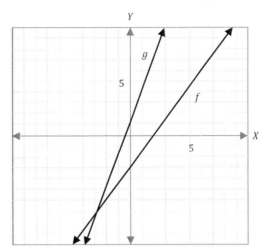

Which statement describes the changes that were made to the graph of f to make the graph of g?

A. The slope was multiplied by -2, and the y −intercept was decreased by 4 to make the graph of g.

B. The slope was multiplied by $-\frac{1}{2}$, and the y −intercept was decreased by 4 to make the graph of g.

C. The slope was multiplied by 2, and the y −intercept was increased by 4 to make the graph of g.

D. The slope was multiplied by $\frac{1}{2}$, and the y −intercept was increased by 4 to make the graph of g.

13) If $f(x) = 3x + 4(x + 1) + 2$ then $f(4x) =$

   A. $28x + 6$
   B. $16x - 6$
   C. $25x + 4$
   D. $12x + 3$

14) What is the solution to the system of equations below?
$$3x + y = 15$$
$$-2x + 4y = 10$$

   A. $\left(\frac{25}{7}, \frac{7}{30}\right)$
   B. $\left(\frac{25}{7}, \frac{30}{7}\right)$
   C. There is no solution.
   D. There is an infinite number of solutions.

15) The complete graph of function f is shown in the $xy-$plane below. For what value of x is the value of $f(x)$ at its minimum?

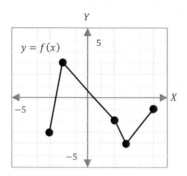

A. -4

B. -3

C. 2

D. 3

16) What is the solution to $1 + 3(m - 4) = 7m$?

A. $m = -11$

B. $m = 2.75$

C. $m = -2.75$

D. $m = 11$

17) The graph of the quadratic function g passes through the points $(-3,0)$, $(-1,4)$, $(0,3)$, and $(2,-5)$. Which of the following shows the same relationship as g?

A. $g(x) = x^2 + 2x - 3$

B.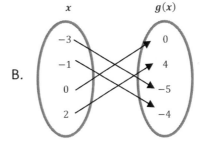

C.

x	$g(x)$
0	-3
4	-1
4	0
-5	2

D.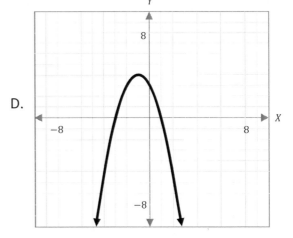

18) A table of values for the exponential function g is shown below.

x	$g(x)$
1	10,000
2	9,750
3	9,506
4	9,269
5	9,037

Which situation could describe this function?

A. The value of a car increases by approximately $2\frac{1}{2}\%$ per year.

B. The value of a house increases by $250 per year.

C. The value of a house decreases by approximately $2\frac{1}{2}\%$ per year.

D. The value of a house decreases by $250 per year.

19) The following table shows the fruits that are given to students of two classes. What fraction of the students of class 2 are given only apples? (Fruits are given to students in 2 classes)

	Peach	Apple	Total
Class 1	14	11	25
Class 2	9	14	23
Total	23	25	48

A. $\frac{14}{23}$

B. $\frac{14}{25}$

C. $\frac{11}{25}$

D. $\frac{23}{48}$

20) The functions g and h are defined below. What is the value of $h(0)$?

$$g(x) = 2x - 1$$
$$h(x) = 1 - g(x)$$

A. -2

B. 0

C. 1

D. 2

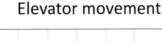

21) The graph below shows the height of an elevator in a tower that moves downwards at a constant rate.

Elevator movement

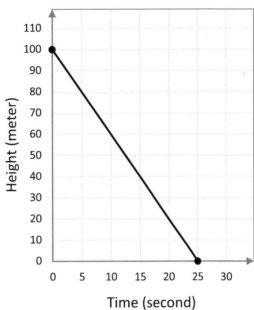

If the rate at which the moved elevator is changed to 6.25 meters per second, how would the amount of time the elevator takes to go down from the top floor of the tower to the ground floor be affected?

A. It would take 9 fewer seconds.

B. It would take 2.25 more seconds.

C. It would take 15 fewer seconds.

D. It would take 6 more seconds.

22) Which function is equivalent to $g(x) = x^2 + 13x - 30$?

A. $g(x) = (x - 2)(x + 15)$

B. $g(x) = (x - 6)(x + 5)$

C. $g(x) = (x - 5)(x + 6)$

D. $g(x) = (x + 2)(x - 15)$

23) A teacher made the scatterplot below to show the number of mistakes his students had as it relates to the average number of study hours per week.

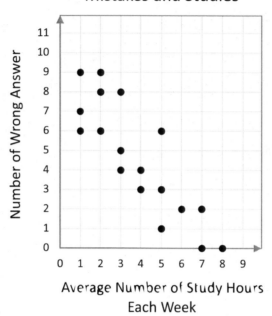

Which of the following best describes the correlation for the data?

A. Positive correction

B. Nonlinear correction

C. Negative correction

D. No correction

Keystone Algebra I Practice Test 8

2024

Part 2

Total number of questions: 4

Total time: No time limit

You may use a calculator on this part.

127

24) If $x^2 + 6x + r$ factors into $(x + 2)(x + p)$, and r and p are constants, what is the value of r?

25) The function f is shown in the figure below. The function g is perpendicular to the function f at the point $(0,4)$. What is the value of x on the point where the function g meets the x −axis?

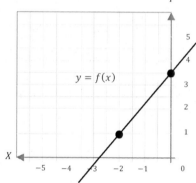

26) A store opened with 12 employees. The store's growth plan assumes that 5 new employees will be hired each year, for the first 7 years. If an equation is written in the form $E = cy + d$ to represent the number of employees, E, employed by the store y years after the store opened, what is the value of d?

27) In the xy−plane, the graph of $y = 4x^2 - 3x$ intersects the graph of $y = -x$ at the points $(0,0)$ and $(c, -c)$. What is the value of c?

End of Keystone Algebra I Practice Test 8

Keystone Algebra I Practice Test 9

2024

Two Parts

Total number of questions: 27

Part 1: 23 questions

Part 2: 4 questions

Total time: No time limit

131

Keystone Algebra I Practice Test Answer Sheet

Remove (or photocopy) this answer sheet and use it to complete the practice test.

Keystone Algebra I Practice Test 9 Answer Sheet

1	Ⓐ Ⓑ Ⓒ Ⓓ	21	Ⓐ Ⓑ Ⓒ Ⓓ
2	Ⓐ Ⓑ Ⓒ Ⓓ	22	Ⓐ Ⓑ Ⓒ Ⓓ
3	Ⓐ Ⓑ Ⓒ Ⓓ	23	Ⓐ Ⓑ Ⓒ Ⓓ
4	Ⓐ Ⓑ Ⓒ Ⓓ	24	
5	Ⓐ Ⓑ Ⓒ Ⓓ	25	
6	Ⓐ Ⓑ Ⓒ Ⓓ	26	
7	Ⓐ Ⓑ Ⓒ Ⓓ	27	
8	Ⓐ Ⓑ Ⓒ Ⓓ		
9	Ⓐ Ⓑ Ⓒ Ⓓ		
10	Ⓐ Ⓑ Ⓒ Ⓓ		
11	Ⓐ Ⓑ Ⓒ Ⓓ		
12	Ⓐ Ⓑ Ⓒ Ⓓ		
13	Ⓐ Ⓑ Ⓒ Ⓓ		
14	Ⓐ Ⓑ Ⓒ Ⓓ		
15	Ⓐ Ⓑ Ⓒ Ⓓ		
16	Ⓐ Ⓑ Ⓒ Ⓓ		
17	Ⓐ Ⓑ Ⓒ Ⓓ		
18	Ⓐ Ⓑ Ⓒ Ⓓ		
19	Ⓐ Ⓑ Ⓒ Ⓓ		
20	Ⓐ Ⓑ Ⓒ Ⓓ		

Keystone Algebra I Practice Test 9

2024

Part 1

Total number of questions: 23

Total time: No time limit

You may use a calculator on this part.

133

1) The function $g(x)$ is defined by a polynomial. Some values of x and $g(x)$ are shown in the table below. Which of the following must be a factor of $g(x)$?

x	$g(x)$
-1	0
0	2
1	-5
5	0

A. $x + 1$
B. $x - 2$
C. $x + 2$
D. $x + 5$

2) If 29 wooden sheets were stacked on top of each other in a column, the column would be approximately $60\frac{3}{5}$ centimeters tall. At this rate, which of the following is closest to the number of wooden sheets it would take to make a 122-centimeter-tall column?
A. 40
B. 59
C. 80
D. 110

3) Which of the following inequality statements represents the set of possible values for the variable "w" that satisfies the inequality $2w + 4z \leq 28$, where $z = -5$?
A. $w \leq 24$
B. $w \leq -24$
C. $w \geq 24$
D. $w \geq -24$

4) The set of ordered pairs below represents some points on the graph of function f.
$$\{(3,2), (0, -1), (-2,7), (-1,2), (5,14)\}$$
What is the parent function of f?
A. $y = x$
B. $y = x^2$
C. $y = 3^x$
D. $y = \sqrt{x}$

5) A basketball player scored at least 15 points more than the previous record for the most points scored in a game. Which inequality can be used to find all possible values of p, the number of points the player scored, in terms of r, the previous record?
   A. $p \leq r - 15$
   B. $p \geq r + 15$
   C. $p \leq 2r$
   D. $p \geq 2r + 15$

6) An engineer is designing a suspension bridge with n sections. The length of each section is $48.2m$. The bridge will also have two towers, each of which is $125.6m$ tall. Which function can be used to find the total length of the bridge in meters, including the towers?
   A. $L(x) = 48.2n + 125.6$
   B. $L(x) = 251.2 + 48.2n$
   C. $L(x) = 48.2n - 125.6$
   D. $L(x) = 173.8n$

7) The equation $2x^2 + 3 = 3x$ has how many distinct real solutions?
   A. 0
   B. 1
   C. 2
   D. 3

8) What are the x −intercepts of the graph of the quadratic function $g(x) = -3x^2 + 9x - 6$?
   A. $(-1,0)$ and $(3,0)$
   B. $(-2,0)$ and $(2,0)$
   C. $(-1,0)$ and $(2,0)$
   D. $(1,0)$ and $(2,0)$

9) Which of the following is equivalent to $8^{\frac{2}{5}}$?
   A. $\sqrt[2]{8}$
   B. $\sqrt[5]{8}$
   C. $4\sqrt{2}$
   D. $2\sqrt[5]{2}$

10) The graph of $y = -3x^2 + 12x + 6$ is shown below. If the graph crosses the y −axis at the point $(0, r)$, what is the value of r?

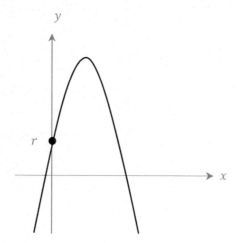

 A. 2

 B. 3

 C. 6

 D. 12

11) A helicopter delivers only 100-pound packages and 120-pound packages. For each delivery trip, the helicopter must carry at least 10 packages, and the total weight of the packages can be at most 1,100 pounds. What is the maximum number of 120-pound packages that the helicopter can carry per trip?

 A. 2

 B. 4

 C. 5

 D. 6

12) What is the equation of the line that has a slope of 2 and passes through the point $(3,5)$?

 A. $y = 2x - 1$

 B. $y = 2x + 1$

 C. $x = 2y - 1$

 D. $x = 2y + 1$

13) The graph of an equation in the form $y = mx + b$ is shown on the grid.

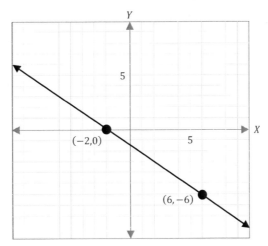

Based on the graph, what is the value of x when $y = 3$?

A. 3

B. 6

C. -3

D. -6

14) Which of the following equation relates y to x for the values in the table below?

x	y
2	$\frac{8}{5}$
3	$\frac{21}{10}$
4	$\frac{13}{5}$
5	$\frac{31}{10}$

A. $y = \frac{1}{2}x + \frac{3}{5}$

B. $y = \frac{3}{5}x + 2$

C. $y = \left(\frac{1}{2}\right)^x + \frac{2}{5}$

D. $y = \left(\frac{1}{3}\right)^{\frac{3}{5}x}$

15) Two functions are given below.

$$f(x) = -2x + 5$$
$$g(x) = -\frac{1}{2}x + 3$$

How does the graph of f compare with the graph of g?

A. The graph of f is less steep than the graph of g.

B. The graph of f has the same $y-$intercept as the graph of g.

C. The graph of f is parallel to the graph of g.

D. The graph of f is steeper than the graph of g.

16) The total cost of renting a bicycle from a rental shop is a function of the number of hours the bicycle is rented. The owner of the rental shop charges $10 per hour up to a maximum of 5 hours plus a $15 late fee. What is the greatest value in the range for this situation?

A. 75

B. 65

C. 60

D. 50

17) A small town's average monthly electricity consumption is 500 kilowatt-hours (kWh). In the first six months of this year, the town consumed a total of 2,800kWh. If it is expected to consume between 400 and 550kWh per month for the rest of the year, what is a reasonable number of additional months needed for the town to reach its average annual electricity consumption?

A. 6 months

B. 5 months

C. 4 months

D. 7 months

18) An airplane's altitude in feet during its descent for landing can be found using the function $f(x) = -200x + 20,000$, where x represents the horizontal distance in miles from where the plane begins its descent. After new government regulations become law, the airplane's descent will be modeled by the function $g(x) = -200x + 21,000$. Which statement describes this change?

A. The airplane starts its descent from an altitude 1,000 feet higher.

B. The airplane starts its descent from an altitude 1,000 feet lower.

C. The airplane descends 1,000 feet per horizontal mile faster.

D. The airplane descends 1,000 feet per horizontal mile slower.

19) The formula below shows the relation between the temperature of food inside a microwave a and the time that takes to heat food up b. Which of the following expresses the time in terms of the temperature of food? $a = 2.35b + 29$

A. $b = \dfrac{a - 2.35}{29}$

B. $b = \dfrac{a - 29}{2.35}$

C. $b = \dfrac{2.35}{a - 29}$

D. $b = \dfrac{2.35}{a + 29}$

20) A movie theater sells tickets for \$9.00 each for adults and \$6.50 each for children. If the theater sold a total of 300 tickets for revenue between \$2250 and \$2500, which inequality represents the possible number of adult tickets sold?

A. $120 \le a \le 200$

B. $80 \le a \le 220$

C. $120 \le a \le 220$

D. $80 \le a \le 200$

21) The table represents some points on the graph of linear function f.

x	$f(x)$
9	288
5	160
4	128
2	64

Which situation can be modeled by this function?

A. The cost in dollars of buying x items that cost \$64 each

B. The number of miles a train had traveled after leaving the station at 32 miles per hour for x hours

C. The remaining number of miles on a 224-mile trip after traveling 32 miles per hour for x hours

D. The amount owed on a \$288 loan after paying \$64 per month for x months

22) The cost of shipping a package varies directly with its weight. The cost of shipping a 4-pound package is \$10.80. What is the cost, in dollars, of shipping a 2.5-pound package?

A. \$6.75

B. \$5.40

C. \$8.50

D. \$3.60

23) A boutique store has a total of 200 dresses on display. The ratio of the number of evening dresses to the number of cocktail dresses on display is $3:5$. How many evening and cocktail dresses are on display?

    A. 50 evening dresses and 150 cocktail dresses

    B. 75 evening dresses and 125 cocktail dresses

    C. 90 evening dresses and 110 cocktail dresses

    D. 100 evening dresses and 100 cocktail dresses

STOP

This is the End of this Section.

Keystone Algebra I Practice Test 9

2024

Part 2

Total number of questions: 4

Total time: No time limit

You may use a calculator on this part.

141

24) The line k is parallel to the line $y = \frac{3}{4}x + 3$ and intersects the y-axis at point -7. If point $m(12, b)$ is on the line k, what is the value of b?

25) Kilometers and miles are units of measure of length. They are directly proportional such that 10 miles are equal to 16 kilometers. How much length, in kilometers, is equal to 50 miles?

26) What is the value of x in the following system of equations?
$$x + y = 7$$
$$x + 2y = 11$$

27) Tasha would owe $19,200 in taxes each year. This year, Tasha is eligible for tax deductions that reduce the tax amount she owes by $1,536.00. If these tax deductions reduce the taxes Tasha owes this year by $x\%$, what is the value of x?

End of Keystone Algebra I Practice Test 9

Keystone Algebra I Practice Test 10

2024

Two Parts

Total number of questions: 27

Part 1: 23 questions

Part 2: 4 questions

Total time: No time limit

145

Keystone Algebra I Practice Test Answer Sheet

Remove (or photocopy) this answer sheet and use it to complete the practice test.

Keystone Algebra I Practice Test 10 Answer Sheet

1 (A) (B) (C) (D)	21 (A) (B) (C) (D)
2 (A) (B) (C) (D)	22 (A) (B) (C) (D)
3 (A) (B) (C) (D)	23 (A) (B) (C) (D)
4 (A) (B) (C) (D)	24
5 (A) (B) (C) (D)	25
6 (A) (B) (C) (D)	26
7 (A) (B) (C) (D)	27
8 (A) (B) (C) (D)	
9 (A) (B) (C) (D)	
10 (A) (B) (C) (D)	
11 (A) (B) (C) (D)	
12 (A) (B) (C) (D)	
13 (A) (B) (C) (D)	
14 (A) (B) (C) (D)	
15 (A) (B) (C) (D)	
16 (A) (B) (C) (D)	
17 (A) (B) (C) (D)	
18 (A) (B) (C) (D)	
19 (A) (B) (C) (D)	
20 (A) (B) (C) (D)	

Keystone Algebra I Practice Test 10

2024

Part 1

Total number of questions: 23

Total time: No time limit

You may use a calculator on this part.

147

1) A graph of $f(x) = 8x^2 - 2x - 3$ is shown on the grid.

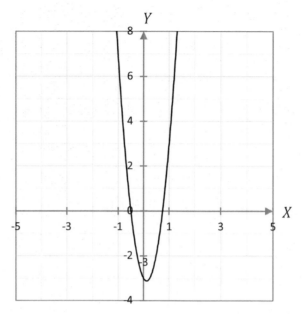

What are the zeros of f?

A. 1

B. $-\frac{1}{2}$ and $\frac{3}{4}$

C. -3

D. $\frac{1}{2}$ and $\frac{3}{4}$

2) Which situation can be represented by $y = 5x + 7$?

A. The number of cookies, y, in x dozens of cookies after 7 cookies are added to each dozen.

B. The number of people, y, in x groups of 5 people each after adding 7 more people to each group.

C. The cost, y, after a \$7 discount, of buying x jackets that sell for \$5 each.

D. The number of inches, y, in an x-foot-tall tree after adding 7 inches to its height.

3) Which expression is a factor of $6x^2 + x - 2$?

A. $2x + 1$

B. $3x - 2$

C. $3 - 2x$

D. $1 - 2x$

4) Which of the following is equivalent to $(5n^2 + 4n + 8) - (n + 2 - 3n^2)$?

   A. $n + 4n^2$

   B. $n^2 - 12$

   C. $8n^2 + 3n + 6$

   D. $3n+6$

5) Which graph represents the solution set of $x < \frac{5}{2}y + 5$?

A.
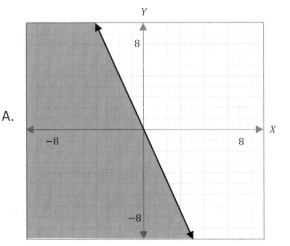

B.
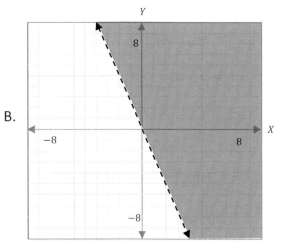

C.
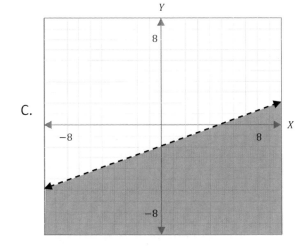

D.
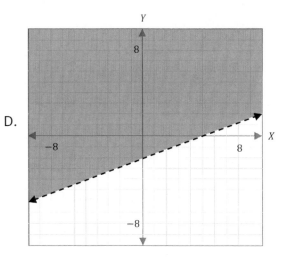

6) What is the value of x in the following equation? $\frac{3}{4}(x - 2) = 3\left(\frac{1}{6}x - \frac{3}{2}\right)$

   A. $\frac{1}{4}$

   B. $-\frac{3}{4}$

   C. -3

   D. -12

7) Which inequality is equivalent to $4x - 3y < 2y + 35$?

A. $y > 0.8x - 7$

B. $y < 0.8x - 7$

C. $y > 7 - 0.8x$

D. $y < 7 - 0.8x$

8) In the equation below, which of the following is a possible value of $x + 3$? $(x > -1)$

$$x + 3 = \frac{11(x + 1)}{(x^2 + 4x + 3)}$$

A. -1

B. 3

C. $\sqrt{11}$

D. 15

9) Mr. Anderson has a beaker containing n milliliters of the solution to distribute to the students in his chemistry class. If he gives each student 3 milliliters of the solution, he will have 5 milliliters left over. In order to give each student 4 milliliters of the solution, he will need an additional 21 milliliters. How many students are in the class?

A. 16

B. 21

C. 23

D. 26

10) The diagram shows the floor plan of a storage facility. All dimensions are given in feet.

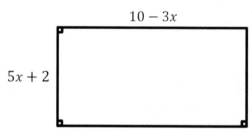

$10 - 3x$

$5x + 2$

Which expression represents the area of the storage facility in square feet?

A. $15x^2 + 44x + 20$

B. $-15x^2 + 44x - 20$

C. $44x + 20 - 15x^2$

D. $-15x^2 - 44x + 20$

11) If the system of inequalities $y < 2x + 6$ and $y \leq \frac{1}{2}x - 2$ is graphed in the $xy-$plane below, which quadrant contains no solutions to the system?

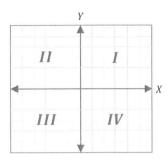

A. Quadrant II

B. Quadrant III

C. Quadrant IV

D. There are solutions in all four quadrants.

12) Which function is equivalent to $h(x) = 2x^2 - 7x - 30$?

A. $h(x) = (2x - 5)(x + 6)$

B. $h(x) = (2x - 6)(x + 5)$

C. $h(x) = (2x + 5)(x - 6)$

D. $h(x) = (2x + 6)(x - 5)$

13) The number of stores opened by a food company can be modeled by the exponential function graphed on the grid, where x is the number of years since 2005.

Food Stores

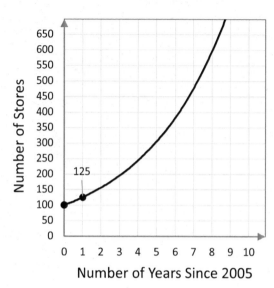

Based on the graph, which statement does not appear to be true?

A. The food company had opened 100 stores by the end of 2005.

B. The food company opened more than 150 stores in one year.

C. Every year the number of stores the food company opened increased by 25%.

D. Since 2005 the food company has opened 50 stores each year.

14) The table represents some points on the graph of linear function f.

x	$f(x)$
-3	-7
-1	-1
2	8
4	14

The graph of f was translated left 7 units to create the graph of function g. Which statement comparing the graphs of f and g is true?

A. The x −intercept of the graph of f is 7 units to the up of the x −intercept of the graph of g.

B. The graph of g is steeper than the graph of g.

C. The y −intercept of the graph of f is 21 units down the y −intercept of the graph of g.

D. The graph of f is less steep than the graph of g.

15) The graph illustrates how the number of presentations made by a convention presenter relates to the number of cookies she had left to give away.

What does the x −intercept of the graph represent?

Cookies at Presentation

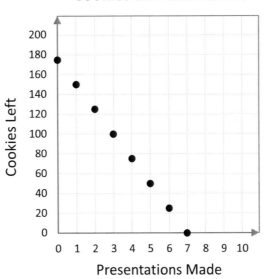

A. The initial number of cookies the presenter had before making any presentations.

B. The point at which the presenter stopped giving away cookies during the presentations.

C. The rate at which the presenter made presentations per unit of time.

D. The maximum number of presentations the presenter made before running out of cookies.

16) An online tutoring service charges a fixed monthly fee of $50 plus an hourly fee of $20 for each tutoring session. The total amount of money a customer spends on tutoring in dollars in a single month can be found using the function $y = 20x + 50$. What does the variable x represent in this function?

A. The total amount of money the customer spends on tutoring each month

B. The number of hours the customer spends on tutoring each month

C. The number of tutors the customer works with each month

D. The hourly fee charged by the tutoring service

17) The following table represents the value of x and function $f(x)$. Which of the following could be the equation of the function $f(x)$?

A. $7 - 2x$

B. $2x^2 + 1$

C. $1 + 2^x$

D. $(x - 1)^2$

x	$f(x)$
-2	1.25
0	2
1	3
2	5

18) A football team had \$20,000 to spend on supplies. The team spent \$14,000 on new balls. New sports shoes cost \$120 each. Which of the following inequalities represents the number of new shoes the team can purchase?

A. $120x - 14,000 \le 20,000$

B. $120x + 14,000 \le 20,000$

C. $120x + 14,000 \ge 20,000$

D. $14,000x - 120 \le 20,000$

19) The graph below shows the distance traveled d, in feet, by a box inside a truck on a road, t minutes after the box is placed inside the truck. Which of the following equations correctly relates to d and t?

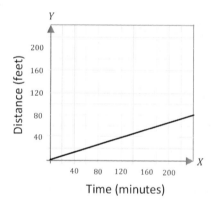

A. $d = 3t$

B. $d = t + 3$

C. $d = \frac{1}{3}t$

D. $d = 3t + 3$

20) There are 97 students in a classroom. There are 15 more girls than boys. What is the total number of girls in the classroom?

A. 97

B. 82

C. 41

D. 56

21) The formula below is used in medicine to estimate the body surface area A, in square meters, of infants and children whose weight w ranges between 3 and 30 kilograms and whose height h is measured in centimeters. Based on the current formula, what is w in terms of A?

Current's formula: $A = \frac{4+w}{30}$

A. $w = 30A - 4$

B. $w = 30A + 4$

C. $w = 30(A - 4)$

D. $w = 30A + 4$

22) Which set of ordered pairs represents x as a function of y?

A. $\{(-9,2), (0,6,), (1,-2,), (-3,6,)\}$

B. $\{(-1,0), (4,3), (-7,-3), (-1,-8)\}$

C. $\{(3,2), (-4,-2), (3,1), (-4,1)\}$

D. $5,4,2,3,1,1,2,4$

23) What is the y −intercept of the graph $g(x) = 0.7(2.3)^x$?

A. 0.7

B. 2.3

C. 0

D. 3

STOP
This is the End of this Section.

Keystone Algebra I Practice Test 10

2024

Part 2

Total number of questions: 4

Total time: No time limit

You may use a calculator on this part.

156

24) The score on a TV contest is obtained by subtracting the number of incorrect answers from three times the number of correct answers. If a player answered 50 questions and obtained a score of 110, how many questions did the player answer correctly?

25) The graph of $y = f(x)$ in the xy −plane is shown below. What is the value of $f(-4)$?

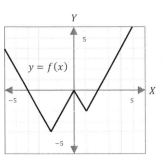

26) If $h^{\frac{k}{6}} = 125$ for positive integers h and k, What is the smallest possible value subtracted from the largest possible value for k?

27) The system of equations below has no solutions. If a and b are constants, what is the value of $\frac{a}{b}$?

$$\frac{3}{4}x - \frac{1}{2}y = 12$$
$$ax - by = 9$$

End of Keystone Algebra I Practice Test 10

Keystone Algebra I Practice Tests Answer Keys

Now, it's time to review your results to see where you went wrong and what areas you need to improve.

Keystone Algebra I Practice Test 1				Keystone Algebra I Practice Test 2			
Section 1		Section 2		Section 1		Section 2	
1	D	24	11.5	1	C	24	3
2	A	25	7	2	D	25	$\frac{7}{2}$
3	A	26	-2	3	D	26	63
4	D	27	$-\frac{3}{2}$	4	D	27	30
5	A			5	A		
6	C			6	B		
7	C			7	D		
8	B			8	C		
9	C			9	B		
10	B			10	B		
11	C			11	C		
12	C			12	D		
13	D			13	C		
14	A			14	D		
15	A			15	D		
16	A			16	D		
17	C			17	D		
18	B			18	B		
19	C			19	B		
20	A			20	C		
21	A			21	B		
22	D			22	B		
23	C			23	D		

Keystone Algebra I Practice Test 3				Keystone Algebra I Practice Test 4			
Section 1		**Section 2**		**Section 1**		**Section 2**	
1	A	**24**	2	**1**	C	**24**	9
2	D	**25**	−5	**2**	C	**25**	−3
3	D	**26**	−1	**3**	A	**26**	42
4	C	**27**	1	**4**	A	**27**	−2
5	D			**5**	A		
6	D			**6**	D		
7	C			**7**	A		
8	C			**8**	C		
9	B			**9**	D		
10	B			**10**	A		
11	C			**11**	C		
12	A			**12**	D		
13	A			**13**	D		
14	D			**14**	B		
15	D			**15**	A		
16	D			**16**	C		
17	C			**17**	B		
18	B			**18**	A		
19	C			**19**	C		
20	B			**20**	D		
21	A			**21**	B		
22	A			**22**	D		
23	B			**23**	B		

Keystone Algebra I Practice Test 5				Keystone Algebra I Practice Test 6			
Section 1		Section 2		Section 1		Section 2	
1	A	24	42	1	C	24	4
2	B	25	−3	2	B	25	6
3	B	26	−9	3	C	26	15
4	D	27	10	4	A	27	14
5	A			5	C		
6	A			6	B		
7	D			7	B		
8	B			8	D		
9	C			9	D		
10	C			10	D		
11	C			11	D		
12	C			12	B		
13	B			13	D		
14	D			14	C		
15	D			15	B		
16	B			16	C		
17	B			17	B		
18	C			18	D		
19	A			19	C		
20	B			20	B		
21	D			21	A		
22	C			22	D		
23	D			23	C		

Keystone Algebra I Practice Test 7				Keystone Algebra I Practice Test 8			
Section 1		**Section 2**		**Section 1**		**Section 2**	
1	C	**24**	4	**1**	D	**24**	8
2	D	**25**	4	**2**	D	**25**	6
3	B	**26**	3	**3**	B	**26**	12
4	B	**27**	39,366	**4**	A	**27**	$\frac{1}{2}$
5	C			**5**	C		
6	D			**6**	D		
7	D			**7**	B		
8	B			**8**	A		
9	C			**9**	D		
10	C			**10**	B		
11	A			**11**	C		
12	C			**12**	C		
13	B			**13**	C		
14	A			**14**	A		
15	A			**15**	B		
16	B			**16**	D		
17	D			**17**	C		
18	D			**18**	D		
19	C			**19**	A		
20	A			**20**	D		
21	D			**21**	A		
22	D			**22**	A		
23	B			**23**	C		

Keystone Algebra I Practice Tests Answers and Explanations

Keystone Algebra I Practice Tests 1 Explanations
Section 1

1) Choice D is correct

The equation of the quadratic function $y = 3x^2 - 6x$ is in the standard form $y = ax^2 + bx + c$. So, the axis of symmetry is obtained from the formula $x = \frac{-b}{2a}$. Therefore, the axis of symmetry of this function is $x = \frac{-(-6)}{2(3)} \to x = 1$.

Factor as follow: $3x^2 - 6x = 3x(x) - 3x(2) = 3x(x - 2)$. That is, the factors of g are x and $x - 2$. By calculating $g(x) = 0$, the zeros of the equation are 0 and 2. Because,

$$g(x) = 0 \to 3x(x - 2) = 0 \to x = 0 \text{ and } x = 2.$$

There is no vertical axis of symmetry for quadratic functions, with the equation $y = ax^2 + bx$. Then, the choice D is correct.

2) Choice A is correct

Factor the expression: $12x^8 - 21x^4 + 3x^3 = 3x^3(4x^5 - 7x + 1)$. Therefore, the correct listed factor is $4x^5 - 7x + 1$.

3) Choice A is correct

Since the line is horizontal, the equation of the line is in the form of $y = b$, where y takes the same value of 12. Thus, the equation of the line is $y = 12$.

4) Choice D is correct

Remember that the range of an arbitrary function is an image of the graph on the $y-$axis. We know that the ordered pair $(2,4)$ is not on the graph and the range of an exponential function is the interval $(0, +\infty)$ that is, the point 0 is not in the range of an exponential function. So, the

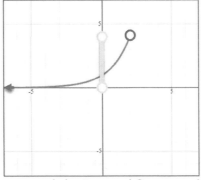

image of the graph on the y-axis covered the interval $0 < y < 4$.

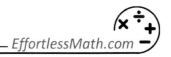

5) Choice A is correct

Use the FOIL (First, Out, In, Last) method:

$$(7x + 2y)(5x + 2y) = 35x^2 + 14xy + 10xy + 4y^2$$
$$= 35x^2 + 24xy + 4y^2$$

6) Choice C is correct

All the ordered pairs that satisfy in equation $f(x) = 5x^2 - 30x - 4$, must also be true in the equivalent equation. So. It's enough, put some point of this equation in the choices and check the results. For the function $f(x)$, if $x = 0$ and $x = -1$, then $f(0) = 5(0)^2 - 30(0) - 4 = -4$ and $f(-1) = 5(-1)^2 - 30(-1) - 4 = 31$. Now, we have:

 A. $f(0) = 5(0 - 3)^2 + 49 = 5(9) + 49 = 94 \neq -4$. It's Not true!

 B. $f(0) = 5(0 + 3)^2 - 49 = 5(9) - 49 = -4 = -4$

 C. $f(0) = 5(0 - 3)^2 - 49 = 5(9) - 49 = -4 = -4$

 D. $f(0) = 5(0 - 49)^2 - 3 = 5(2,401) - 3 = 12,002 \neq -4$. It's Not true!

In this case, plug $x = -1$ in the remaining equations:

 B. $f(-1) = 5(-1 + 3)^2 - 49 = 5(4) - 49 = -29 \neq 31$. It's Not true.

 C. $f(-1) = 5(-1 - 3)^2 - 49 = 5(16) - 49 = 31$. This is true!

7) Choice C is correct

If there is a line parallel to the $y-$axis that intersects the graph at more than one point, then that graph does not represent a function. Clearly, the graph of choices A, B, and D are shown the graph of a straight line, a quadratic equation, and an exponential. Then these graphs are function.

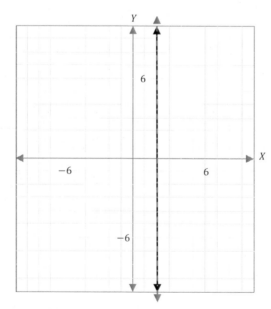

In the case of choice C, the line shown in the graph intersects the graph at more than one point, so it is not a function.

8) Choice B is correct

Since the sign of the inequality is less than $<$, then the corresponding graph has a dashed line. That is, the choices of either B or C are the possible choices. Substitute the point $(0,0)$ of the graph area A in the given inequality. So,

$$(0,0) \rightarrow 0 < 3 - 2(0) \rightarrow 0 < 3.$$

Therefore, choice B is the correct answer because the point $(0,0)$ from the area of B applies to the inequality.

9) Choice C is correct

According to the first characteristic, one of the choices of either B or C can be the right choice. Since the graph has two zeros, then the points where the graph intersects the x −axis is two points. Therefore, only choice C is correct. The graph below shows the desired characteristics of choice C.

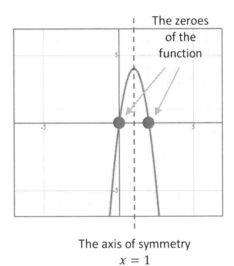

The axis of symmetry
$$x = 1$$

10) Choice B is correct

Since the number of hours worked for the first and second jobs is represented by x and y respectively and the sum of her hours worked per month is not more than 192 hours, it can be shown that her hours are worked as $x + y \leq 192$. To graph the recent model, first, draw the line graph of the equation of $x + y = 192$.

One of the choices of either B or D is the answer. Now, by substituting some points on the shaded area of graphs B and D in the inequality $x + y \leq 192$, you can determine the correct graph. (For example, the points marked in the previous graph.)

B. $(24,96) \rightarrow 24 + 96 = 120 \leq 192$. This ordered pair on the shaded area of B satisfies the inequality.

D. $(120,144) \rightarrow 120 + 144 = 264 \nleq 192$. This point on the shaded area of D does not satisfy the inequality.

Then, the graph B is the correct answer.

11) Choice C is correct

Given the content of the question, since a linear function can be used to model the data, the rate of change is the same for most points. Therefore, to obtain the slope of the linear function for data modeling, evaluate the rate of change for several points. Use the formula of the rate of change $\frac{f(b)-f(a)}{b-a}$. So,

If $a = 840$ and $b = 3,280$, then $\frac{f(b)-f(a)}{b-a} = \frac{82-21}{3,280-840} = 0.025$,

If $a = 1,480$ and $b = 3,280$, then $\frac{f(b)-f(a)}{b-a} = \frac{82-37}{3,280-1,480} = 0.025$,

If $a = 840$ and $b = 2,600$, then $\frac{f(b)-f(a)}{b-a} = \frac{63-21}{2,600-840} \cong 0.024$,

If $a = 480$ and $b = 1,280$, then $\frac{f(b)-f(a)}{b-a} = \frac{32-12}{1,280-480} = 0.025$.

Now write the linear equation with slope $m = 0.025$. Therefore, the linear equation of the function of this model is $y = 0.025x$. In this case, substitute $x = 4,000$ and calculate the number of feedbacks.

$$x = 4,000 \rightarrow y = 0.025(4,000) = 100.$$

12) Choice C is correct

The slope of the line graph is equivalent to the rate of change. Use formula

$$\text{Rate of change} = \frac{y_2-y_1}{x_2-x_1}$$

For arbitrary points (x_1, y_1) and (x_2, y_2) on the graph.

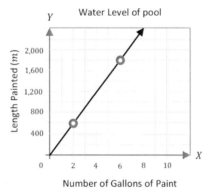

Calculate the rate of change with the marked points in the above graph to the coordinates $(2,600)$ and $(6,1,800)$. So,

$$\text{Rate of change} = \frac{1,800-600}{6-2} = \frac{1,200}{4} = 300$$

13) Choice D is correct

We know that for the function f, if $0 < k < 1$ then the function is compressed vertically. It's equivalent to graph D.

14) Choice A is correct

Since $f(x)$ is a linear function with a negative slope, then when $x = -2$, $f(x)$ is maximum, and when $x = 3$, $f(x)$ is minimum. Then the ratio of the minimum value to the maximum value of the function is: $\frac{f(3)}{f(-2)} = \frac{-3(3)+1}{-3(-2)+1} = \frac{-8}{7} = -\frac{8}{7}$.

15) Choice A is correct

To find the system of equations, write the equation of the line passing through two arbitrary points from the given table and graph, respectively.

For the marked points $\left(-2, -\frac{5}{3}\right)$ and $\left(1, \frac{1}{3}\right)$ of the graph of line g, the slope of the line obtained from the formula $m = \frac{y_2 - y_1}{x_2 - x_1}$, where (x_1, y_1) and (x_2, y_2) are two points on the graph. Then, $m = \frac{\frac{1}{3} - \left(-\frac{5}{3}\right)}{1 - (-2)} = \frac{\frac{6}{3}}{3} = \frac{2}{3}$. Now, use the following formula to write the equation of the line.

$$y - y_1 = m(x - x_1)$$

where m is the slope of the line and (x_1, y_1) is a point on the graph g. So, the equation of the line passing through the point $\left(-2, -\frac{5}{3}\right)$ with the slope $m = \frac{2}{3}$ is as follows:

$$y - \left(-\frac{5}{3}\right) = \frac{2}{3}(x - (-2)) \rightarrow y + \frac{5}{3} = \frac{2}{3}(x + 2) = \frac{2}{3}x + \frac{4}{3} \rightarrow y = \frac{2}{3}x - \frac{1}{3}$$

For points $(-1, 4)$ and $(1, 2)$ of the table of line t, the slope of the line is $m = \frac{2 - 4}{1 - (-1)} = \frac{-2}{2} = -1$. The equation of the line through passing $(1, 2)$ with the slope $m = -1$ is

$$y - 2 = -1(x - 1) \rightarrow y - 2 = -x + 1 \rightarrow y = 3 - x.$$

The system of equations is

$$y = 3 - x$$
$$y = \frac{2}{3}x - \frac{1}{3}$$

16) Choice A is correct

Let x be the number of years, therefore, \$2,000 per year equals $2,000x$. Starting from a \$26,000 annual salary means you should add that amount to $2,000x$. Income more than that is:

$$I > 2,000x + 26,000$$

17) Choice C is correct

Multiply the numerators and denominators: $\frac{3x + 6}{x + 5} \times \frac{x + 5}{x + 2} = \frac{(3x + 6)(x + 5)}{(x + 5)(x + 2)}$

Cancel the common factor: $\frac{(3x + 6)(x + 5)}{(x + 5)(x + 2)} = \frac{(3x + 6)}{(x + 2)}$

Factor $3x + 6 = 3(x + 2)$

Then: $\frac{3(x + 2)}{(x + 2)} = 3$

18) Choice B is correct

Considering the choices, the corresponding function of this graph is exponential. Since the graph is increasing, then the suitable choice has a base greater than 1. That is, the choice A is not the answer. Now, by substituting some points on the graph with the remaining choices and checking to satisfy these points, the correct answer is determined. Try the point $(0,32)$. Therefore,

B. $(0,32) \rightarrow 32(1.5)^0 = 32 = 32$. It's true.

C. $(0,32) \rightarrow 1.5(32)^0 = 1.5 \neq 32$. It's NOT true!

D. $(0,32) \rightarrow 0.67(48)^0 = 0.67 \neq 32$. It's NOT true!

Then, the choice B is the correct answer.

19) Choice C is correct

Multiply by the conjugate: $\frac{\sqrt{12}+3}{\sqrt{12}+3} \rightarrow \frac{6}{\sqrt{12}-3} \times \frac{\sqrt{12}+3}{\sqrt{12}+3}$

$(\sqrt{12}-3)(\sqrt{12}+3) = 3$, then: $\frac{6}{\sqrt{12}-3} \times \frac{\sqrt{12}+3}{\sqrt{12}+3} = \frac{6(\sqrt{12}+3)}{3} = 2(\sqrt{12}+3)$

20) Choice A is correct

The domain of motion of this throw, from the starting point to the point entering the basketball net, is equivalent to the changes of the first component of the ordered pairs. It means that the interval $0 \leq x \leq 14.5$.

21) Choice A is correct

$2x - 5 \geq 3x - 1$, Add 5 to both sides: $2x - 5 + 5 \geq 3x - 1 + 5 \rightarrow 2x \geq 3x + 4$, Subtract $3x$ from both sides: $2x - 3x \geq 3x + 4 - 3x \rightarrow -x \geq +4$, Multiply both sides by -1 (reverse the inequality): $(-x)(-1) \geq (+4)(-1) \rightarrow x \leq -4$. Only -2 is greater than -4.

22) Choice D is correct

Use the difference of squares $a^2 - b^2 = (a + b)(a - b)$. So, $9n^2 - 36 = (3n + 6)(3n - 6)$. It can also be written as: $(3n + 6)(3n - 6) = 3 \times (n + 2) \times 3 \times (n - 2) = 9(n + 2)(n - 2)$.

23) Choice C is correct

To find the y −intercept, put the value of x in the function $g(x)$ equal to zero. Therefore,

$x = 0 \rightarrow g(0) = 25(1.2)^{0+1} = 25(1.2) = 30.$

Keystone Algebra I Practice Tests 1 Explanations
Section 2

24) The y −intercept is 11.5

The y −intercept in a graph is the value that intercepts the y −axis function. For this purpose, calculate the value of the function for $x = 0$. Therefore,

$$x = 0 \rightarrow f(0) = 11.5(0.8)^0 = 11.5 \times 1 = 11.5$$

25) The solution is 7

Add 5 to both sides: $7x - 5 + 5 = 16 + 4x + 5 \rightarrow 7x = 21 + 4x$. Now, subtract $4x$ from both sides: $7x - 4x = 21 + 4x - 4x \rightarrow 3x = 21$. Finally, divide both sides by 3, we have $\frac{3x}{3} = \frac{21}{3} \rightarrow x = 7$.

26) The y −intercept is -2

The y −intercept is the point where the graph intersects the y −axis. The point is shown in the graph below.

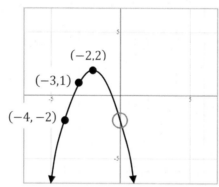

The above quadratic function is symmetric with respect to the axis $x = -2$. So, the ordered pair $(0, -2)$ is the y −intercept.

27) The negative solution is $-\frac{3}{2}$

Simplify the equation $Q(x) = 2x^3 - x^2 - 6x$. First, factor the equation: $2x^3 - x^2 - 6x = x(2x^2 - x - 6)$. To find the zeros, each factor should equal zero: $x(2x^2 - x - 6) = 0$. Therefore, the zeros are $x = 0, 2x^2 - x - 6 = 0$.

At this point, evaluate the discriminant of the quadratic equation $2x^2 - x - 6 = 0$. The expression $\Delta = b^2 - 4ac$ is called the discriminant for the standard form of the quadratic equation as $ax^2 + bx + c = 0$. So, $\Delta = b^2 - 4ac \rightarrow \Delta = (-1)^2 - 4(2)(-6) = 49$.

Since $\Delta > 0$, the quadratic equation has two distinct solutions. Now, use the quadratic formula:

$$x_{1,2} = \frac{-b \pm \sqrt{\Delta}}{2a}$$

Then, the roots are $x_1 = \frac{-(-1)+\sqrt{49}}{2(2)} = \frac{1+7}{4} = 2$, and $x_2 = \frac{-(-1)-\sqrt{49}}{2(2)} = \frac{1-7}{4} = -\frac{3}{2}$.

Keystone Algebra I Practice Tests 2 Explanations
Section 1

1) Choice C is correct

According to the content question, we know that the sum of his hours worked per week is less than 65 hours, it can be shown that his hours worked as $x + y < 65$. First, graph this equation $x + y = 65$ as a dashed line.

Now, put a point on each side of the dashed line in the inequality and check which one satisfies the inequality. (For example, the points marked in the previous graph.)

A. $(60,20) \rightarrow 60 + 20 = 80 \not< 65$. It's NOT true!

C. $(20,20) \rightarrow 20 + 20 = 40 < 65$. It's true.

2) Choice D is correct

The equation of a line is $y = mx + b$, where m is the slope and b is the y-intercept.

First find the slope: $m = \frac{y_2 - y_1}{x_2 - x_1} = \frac{15 - (-5)}{8 - 3} = \frac{20}{5} = 4$. Then, we have: $y = 4x + b$

Choose one point and plug in the values of x and y in the equation to solve for b.

Let's choose the point $(3, -5)$. $y = 4x + b \rightarrow -5 = 4(3) + b \rightarrow -5 = 12 + b \rightarrow b = -17$

The equation of the line is: $y = 4x - 17$

3) Choice D is correct

Use the FOIL (First, Out, In, Last) method:

$$(5x + 2y)(2x - y) = 10x^2 - 5xy + 4xy - 2y^2 = 10x^2 - xy - 2y^2$$

4) Choice D is correct

Notice that the domain of a quadratic function is all real numbers. That is, the answer is either the choices A or D. In addition, you can see that the graph is going downward. Then the range of this function is less than a real number like a. It is equivalent to the inequality $y \leq a$. The only choice that satisfies these conditions is D.

5) Choice A is correct

The equation of a line in slope-intercept form is: $y = mx + b$. Solve for y.

$$4x - 2y = 6 \Rightarrow -2y = 6 - 4x \Rightarrow y = (6 - 4x) \div (-2) \Rightarrow y = 2x - 3.$$

The slope is 2. The slope of the line perpendicular to this line is:

$$m_1 \times m_2 = -1 \Rightarrow 2 \times m_2 = -1 \Rightarrow m_2 = -\frac{1}{2}.$$

6) Choice B is correct

Let x be the number of adult tickets and y be the number of student tickets. Then:

$$x + y = 12, \text{ and } 12.50x + 7.50y = 125.$$

Use the elimination method to solve this system of equations. Multiply the first equation by -7.5 and add it to the second equation.

$$-7.5(x + y = 12) \rightarrow -7.5x - 7.5y = -90.$$

$$\begin{cases} -7.5x - 7.5y = -90 \\ 12.5x + 7.5y = 125 \end{cases} \rightarrow (-7.5x - 7.5y) + (12.5x + 7.5y) = -90 + 125.$$

Therefore: $-7.5x + 12.5x = 35 \rightarrow 5x = 35 \rightarrow x = 7$. There are 7 adult tickets and 5 student tickets.

7) Choice D is correct

The graph of quadratic functions is U −shaped and upward or downward (Choice C cannot be the correct answer). The range of a function is the image of the graph of the function on the y −axis. We draw the graph of functions A, B, and D on the y −axis. Like the figure below.

A. B. D.

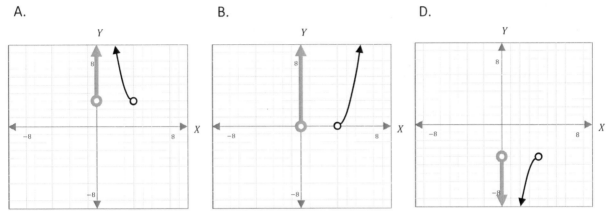

By checking the above figure, we understand that graph D with the range $y < -4$ is a suitable answer.

8) Choice C is correct

First, find the value of b, and then find $f(3)$. Since $f(2) = 35$, substuting 2 for x and 35 for $f(x)$ gives $35 = b(2)^2 + 15 \rightarrow 35 = 4b + 15$. Solving this equation gives $b = 5$. Thus

$$f(x) = 5x^2 + 15, \quad f(3) = 5(3)^2 + 15 \rightarrow f(3) = 45 + 15 \rightarrow f(3) = 60$$

9) Choice B is correct

The rate of change is equal to the slope of the line. Now, evaluate the rate of change using the points indicated with coordinates $(-6, 5)$ and $(3, -1)$ on the graph and the formula of the line slope passing through two points (x_1, y_1) and (x_2, y_2) as $m = \frac{y_2 - y_1}{x_2 - x_1}$. Therefore,

$$\text{Rate of change} = m = \frac{-1 - 5}{3 - (-6)} = \frac{-6}{9} = -\frac{2}{3}.$$

10) Choice B is correct

Select two arbitrary points like $(0,4)$ and $(2,4)$ on the graph. Calculate the slope as $m = \frac{4-4}{2-0} = \frac{0}{2} = 0$. Now, write the equation of the line passing through one point with the slope zero as $y - 4 = 0(x - 2) \rightarrow y = 4$.

11) Choice C is correct

To find the recursive formula, start by looking at the common differences and ratios of consecutive terms. By evaluating the difference between terms with the previous term, you notice that the differences between consecutive terms are all the same. That is, $a_n - a_{n-1} = 4$. In this step, for calculating the first term of the arithmetic sequence, substitute one of the given terms like $a_4 = 19$ and the common difference $d = 4$ in the arithmetic sequence formula: $a_n = a_1 + d(n-1)$, where $a_1 =$ the first term, $d =$ the common difference between terms, $n =$ number of items. Then,

$$a_4 = a_1 + 4(4-1) = 19 \rightarrow a_1 + 12 = 19 \rightarrow a_1 = 7$$

Therefore, the nth term of the sequence is $a_n = 7 + 4(n-1)$. Now, simplify it as

$$a_n = 4n + 3.$$

12) Choice D is correct

It can be seen from the graph that the relationship is downward. Remember that a linear relationship is decreasing whenever the slope of the linear relationship (the coefficient of the independent variable x) is negative.

Now substitute some values from the left column of the table in equations B and D. The equation whose output values are closest to the values in the right column of the table is the best model for describing the data. Check the value $x = 2$. Then,

B. $x = 2 \rightarrow y = -11.5(2) + 8.5 = -23 + 8.5 = -14.5$
D. $x = 2 \rightarrow y = -11.5(2) + 98.7 = -23 + 98.7 = 75.7$

The choice D seems to be appropriate.

13) Choice C is correct

The graph of a system of linear equations has no solution if the lines are parallel. In the graphs, only choice C represents two parallel lines (that are not on top of each other).

14) Choice D is correct

To find the $y-$intercept of a line from its equation, put the equation in slope-intercept form:

$$x - 3y = 12 \rightarrow -3y = -x + 12 \rightarrow 3y = x - 12 \rightarrow y = \frac{1}{3}x - 4$$

The $y-$intercept is what comes after the x. Thus, the $y-$intercept of the line is -4.

15) Choice D is correct

To find the system of equations, need to write the linear equation corresponding to each table. Use the formula:

$$y - y_1 = m(x - x_1)$$

Where $m = \frac{y_2 - y_1}{x_2 - x_1}$ is the slope of the line passing through two points (x_1, y_1) and (x_2, y_2). Choose two ordered pairs like $(4, -2)$ and $(12, 0)$ from the tables. Therefore,

Line L_1: Put $(x_1, y_1) = (4, -2)$ and $(x_2, y_2) = (12, 0)$, then $m = \frac{0 - (-2)}{12 - 4} = \frac{1}{4}$ and

$$y - 0 = \frac{1}{4}(x - 12) \rightarrow y = \frac{1}{4}x - 3$$

Line L_2: Put $(x_1, y_1) = (0, 3)$ and $(x_2, y_2) = (1, 1)$, then $m = \frac{1 - 3}{1 - 0} = -2$ and

$$y - 1 = -2(x - 1) \rightarrow y = -2x + 3$$

The correct answer is $\begin{cases} 4y = x - 12 \\ y = -2x + 3 \end{cases}$.

16) Choice D is correct

Simplify. $7x^2 y^3 (2x^2 y)^3 = 7x^2 y^3 (8x^6 y^3) = 56x^8 y^6$

17) Choice D is correct

First, factor the function: $f(x) = x^3 + 7x^2 + 12x = x(x + 3)(x + 4)$

To find the zeros, $f(x)$ should be zero. $f(x) = x(x + 3)(x + 4) = 0$

Therefore, the zeros are: $x = 0,$ $(x + 3) = 0 \Rightarrow x = -3,$ $(x + 4) = 0 \Rightarrow x = -4$

18) Choice B is correct

$$0.00035 \times (1.2 \times 10^4) = (3.5 \times 10^{-4}) \times (1.2 \times 10^4) = (3.5 \times 1.2) \times (10^{-4} \times 10^4)$$

$$= 4.2 \times 10^{-4+4} = 4.2$$

19) Choice B is correct

The $y-$intercept is the point where the graph intersects the $y-$axis. In the graph, the $y-$axis represents the water level of the lake and the value on the $y-$axis is the initial water level in the decaying relationship. Then the $y-$intercept is the maximum water level and the choice B is true.

20) Choice C is correct

The function $g(x) = -\frac{1}{8}(x - 1)^2 - 3$ is quadratic and the vertex form $y = a(x - h)^2 + k$. So, there is an axis of symmetry parallel to the y −axis that passes through the vertex. The vertex is the point with the coordinate $(h, k) = (1, -3)$. Therefore, the axis of symmetry is $x = 1$.

21) Choice B is correct

The initial value of the car is $35,000. It's equivalent to the ordered pair $(0,35000)$. Since the value of the car decreases at a rate of 20%, then the function is decreasing (the choice C is not true) and for the first year $x = 1$, the value of the function is $y = 35000(0.8)$. Similarly, in the second year $x = 2$, the value of the car is $y = 35000(0.8)(0.8) = 35000(0.8)^2$. Therefore, the model of the relationship can be a part of the function of the form $y = 35000(0.8)^x$ (One of the choices A or B). Now, substitute a few points in the model and check it, until the suitable choice determines.

$$x = 1 \rightarrow y = 35000(0.8)^1 = 28000.$$ It's equivalent to the value of the graph B.

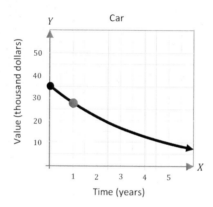

22) Choice B is correct

The sign of inequality is greater than or equal to $\geq$. Therefore, the representation of the corresponding graph must include a line. Pick one of the choices of either B or D. Now, substitute the point $(1,1)$ into the inequality,

$$(1,1) \rightarrow 5(1) + 2(1) \geq 10 \rightarrow 5 + 2 \geq 10 \rightarrow 7 \ngeq 10.$$

It means that the choice B is the answer. Because the point $(1,1)$ is not inside the area shown by B.

23) Choice D is correct

Use this polynomial identity: $x^2 + (a + b)x + ab = (x + a)(x + b)$. Considering the given equation $k^2 - 17k + 66$. We need to find two numbers whose product is 66 and their sum is -17. According to the given choices, these two numbers are -6 and -11 for the above formula as follows:

$$k^2 - 17k + 66 = (k - 6)(k - 11)$$

Keystone Algebra I Practice Tests 2 Explanations
Section 2

24) The value of x is 3

Use the exponential rule: $(x^a)^b = x^{a \times b}$. Then, $(n^2)^3 = n^{2 \times 3} = n^6$. Substitute n^6 in $n^{-3}(n^2)^3$:

$$n^{-3}(n^2)^3 = n^{-3}n^6$$

By using the rule $x^a \times x^b = x^{a+b}$, we have: $n^{-3}n^6 = n^{-3+6} = n^3$. Compare n^3 with n^x. So, the value of x is 3.

25) The positive solution is $\dfrac{7}{2}$

First, simplify the equation $6(x-1)^2 = 41 - x$. Expand the square of the binomial: $(x-1)^2 = (x^2 - 2x + 1)$. Substitute the binomial in the equation

$$6(x^2 - 2x + 1) = 41 - x$$

Then,

$$6x^2 - 12x + 6 = 41 - x$$

Subtract 41 from both sides: $6x^2 - 12x + 6 - 41 = -x \rightarrow 6x^2 - 12x - 35 = -x$. Add x to both sides: $6x^2 - 12x - 35 + x = -x + x \rightarrow 6x^2 - 11x - 35 = 0$.

Now, evaluate the discriminant of the quadratic equation $6x^2 - 11x - 35 = 0$. The expression $\Delta = b^2 - 4ac$ is called the discriminant for the standard form of the quadratic equation as $ax^2 + bx + c = 0$. So, $\Delta = b^2 - 4ac \rightarrow \Delta = (-11)^2 - 4(6)(-35) = 961 > 0$.

Then, the quadratic equation has two distinct solutions. Use the formula

$$x_{1,2} = \frac{-b \pm \sqrt{\Delta}}{2a}$$

Therefore, the roots are $x_1 = \dfrac{-(-11)+\sqrt{961}}{2(6)} = \dfrac{11+31}{12} = \dfrac{7}{2}$, and $x_2 = \dfrac{-(-11)-\sqrt{961}}{2(6)} = \dfrac{11-31}{12} = -\dfrac{5}{3}$.

26) The maximum value of the graph is 63

To find the maximum value of the graph, you need to evaluate the vertex of the quadratic function corresponding to this graph. For this purpose, use the vertex form of a quadratic function as follow:

$$y = a(x-h)^2 + k$$

Where the ordered pair (h, k) is the vertex, and a is a constant number. Now, substitute at least three points on the graph in the vertex form and solve the obtained system of equations. Then:

I. $(0,0) \rightarrow 0 = a(0 - h)^2 + k \rightarrow ah^2 + k = 0$

II. $(13,0) \rightarrow 0 = a(13 - h)^2 + k \rightarrow ah^2 - 26ah + 169a + k = 0$

III. $(4,54) \rightarrow 54 = a(4 - h)^2 + k \rightarrow ah^2 - 8ah + 16a + k = 54$

First, solve the system of equations for $\begin{cases} ah^2 + k = 0 \\ ah^2 - 26ah + 169a + k = 0 \end{cases}$. Subtract the first equation from the second equation. So, $-26ah + 169a = 0 \rightarrow a(-26h + 169) = 0 \rightarrow a = 0$ or $-26h + 169 = 0 \rightarrow 26h = 169 \rightarrow h = 6.5$. Since the function is quadratic, then $a \neq 0$. Therefore, $h = 6.5$. Put $h = 6.5$ in these equations and solve. Now, we have this system of equations $\begin{cases} 42.25a + k = 0 \\ 6.25a + k = 54 \end{cases}$ and solve. Then,

$$6.25a + k - (42.25a + k) = 54 \rightarrow -36a = 54 \rightarrow a = -1.5$$

Finally, put $a = -1.5$ in the first equation. That is, $42.25(-1.5) + k = 0 \rightarrow k = 63.375$. Rounding to the whole number, $k = 63$.

Plug in the values a, h, and k in the vertex form $y = a(x - h)^2 + k$. Therefore,

$$y = -1.5(x - 6.5)^2 + 63$$

where $(6.5, 63.375)$ is at the vertex. It means the maximum value of the graph of the function is $k = 63$.

27) The value of y is 30

Plug in the value of x in the equation and solve for y. $2y = \dfrac{2x^2}{3} + 6 \rightarrow 2y = \dfrac{2(9)^2}{3} + 6 \rightarrow$

$$2y = \dfrac{2(81)}{3} + 6 \rightarrow 2y = 54 + 6 \rightarrow 2y = 60 \rightarrow y = 30.$$

Keystone Algebra I Practice Tests 3 Explanations
Section 1

1) Choice A is correct

The x −intercept of a graph is the point where the graph intersects the x −axis. For the given graph in the question, the points marked in the figure below are x −intercepts.

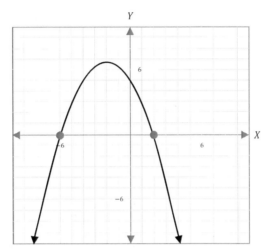

You see that the y −coordinate of these points on the x −axis is 0. So, the coordinate of the x −intercepts are $(-6,0)$ and $(2,0)$. Similarly, we know for y −intercept of a graph that it is the point where the graph intersects the y −axis. We know that the x −coordinate of any point on the y −axis is 0. Therefore,

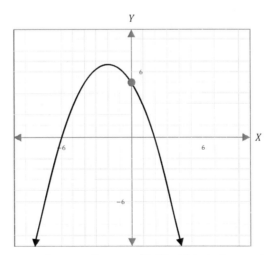

The y −intercept is one point with coordinates $(0,5)$. This information corresponds to choice A.

2) Choice D is correct

To find the graph of the exponential function of the question content, considering that the base of the exponential equation is 0.75 and smaller than 1, we can understand that the function is going down. It means one of the graphs of either A or D is the correct answer. In this case, substitute a few points in the function and check to see if it's correct or not. Choose point 0 and plug it into the function as follow: $y = 8(0.75)^0 = 8$.

That is, the corresponding graph must pass through the ordered pair $(0,8)$. Therefore, the correct answer is D.

3) Choice D is correct

$$x_{1,2} = \frac{-b \pm \sqrt{b^2 - 4ac}}{2a} \quad ax^2 + bx + c = 0$$

$$x^2 + 2x - 5 = 0 \Rightarrow \text{then: } a = 1, b = 2 \text{ and } c = -5$$

$$x = \frac{-2 + \sqrt{2^2 - 4(1)(-5)}}{2(1)} = \sqrt{6} - 1 \qquad x = \frac{-2 - \sqrt{2^2 - 4(1)(-5)}}{2(1)} = -1 - \sqrt{6}$$

4) Choice C is correct

$$\frac{16n^6 - 32n^2 + 8n}{8n} = \frac{16n^6}{8n} - \frac{32n^2}{8n} + \frac{8n}{8n} = 2n^5 - 4n + 1$$

5) Choice D is correct

The sum of the two polynomials is $(4x^2 + 6x - 3) + (3x^2 - 5x + 8)$

This can be rewritten by combining like terms:

$$(4x^2 + 6x - 3) + (3x^2 - 5x + 8) = (4x^2 + 3x^2) + (6x - 5x) + (-3 + 8)$$

$$= 7x^2 + x + 5$$

6) Choice D is correct

Given that the data is related to a linear function and $x = 3$ is the zero of the function, therefore it has a factor of $(x - 3)$. Now, substitute some points like 0 and 4 in choices A and D to determine the correct answer. So,

A. $x = 0 \rightarrow y = -12(0 - 3) = 36$, it's not true.

D. $x = 0 \rightarrow y = 12(0 - 3) = -36$, it's true and correct answer.

7) Choice C is correct

Since the function is quadratic and the graph is going upward, then one of the choices of either C or D is the answer. Because the corresponding function must satisfy all points on the graph. So, substitute a few points like $(0, -3)$ and $(-3,0)$ on the graph in the remaining choices.

C. $(0, -3) \rightarrow \frac{1}{3}(0)^2 - 3 = -3$. It's true.

D. $(0, -3) \rightarrow 3(0)^2 + 3 = 3 \neq -3$. It's NOT true.

8) Choice C is correct

We know that the graph $y = f(x) + k; k > 0$, is shifted k units up of the graph $y = f(x)$, and if $k < 0$, it is shifted k units down. Then, $y = x^2 + 2$ is shifted 2 units up of the graph $y = x^2$. On the other hand, to shift 1 unit to the left, a negative number $k < 0$ must be substituted for k in the equation $y = f(x - k)$. Therefore,

$$n(x) = \left(x - (-1)\right)^2 + 2 \rightarrow n(x) = (x + 1)^2 + 2.$$

9) Choice B is correct

The amount of water in the lake was initially 450,000 cubic meters. It means that the value of f for $w = 0$ is $f(0) = 450,000$. Put $w = 0$ in the choices and compare with $f(0) = 450,000$.

A. $f(0) = 1.03(450,000)^0 = 1.03$

B. $f(0) = 450,000(0.93)^0 = 450,000$

C. $f(0) = 450,000(1.03)^0 450,000$

D. $f(0) = 0.93(450,000)^0 = 0.93$

Then, one of the choices B or C is the solution. Note that in a descending exponential function, the base is less than one. Therefore, choice B is correct.

10) Choice B is correct

Notice that $(bx - a)$ is a factor of an expression whenever $x = \frac{a}{b}$ is a zero of that expression. Check which of the choices is a zero of the expression.

A. $x + 1 = 0 \rightarrow x = -1 \rightarrow 15(-1)^2 - 12(-1) - 3 = 15 + 12 - 3 = 24 \neq 0$

B. $5x + 1 = 0 \rightarrow x = -\frac{1}{5} \rightarrow 15\left(-\frac{1}{5}\right)^2 - 12\left(-\frac{1}{5}\right) - 3 = 15\left(\frac{1}{25}\right) + \frac{12}{5} - 3 = \frac{15+60-75}{25} = 0$

C. $5x - 1 = 0 \to x = \frac{1}{5} \to 15\left(\frac{1}{5}\right)^2 - 12\left(\frac{1}{5}\right) - 3 = 15\left(\frac{1}{25}\right) - \frac{12}{5} - 3 = \frac{15-60-75}{25} = -\frac{24}{5} \neq 0$

D. $3x - 1 = 0 \to x = \frac{1}{3} \to 15\left(\frac{1}{3}\right)^2 - 12\left(\frac{1}{3}\right) - 3 = 15\left(\frac{1}{9}\right) - \frac{12}{3} - 3 = \frac{15-36-27}{9} = -\frac{16}{3} \neq 0$

Therefore, B is the correct answer.

11) Choice C is correct

Since the represented graph of the inequality is shown as a line, so, the sign of inequality is less than or equal to $\leq$ or greater than or equal to $\geq$. Now, to find the inequality of the given graph, substitute a number of points of the solution region into the given inequalities. Substitute $x = 0$, and $y = 0$ into the remaining inequalities, that is the choices of either B or C. Therefore,

B. $(0,0) \to 3(0) + 2(0) \geq 2 \to 0 \geq 2$, this is not true.

C. $(0,0) \to 3(0) - 2(0) \leq 2 \to 0 \leq 2$, this is true and the correct answer.

12) Choice A is correct

First, find the zeros of the function $p(x)$:

$$p(x) = 0 \to (x - 2)(x + 3) = 0 \to x - 2 = 0 \to x = 2, \text{ or } x + 3 = 0 \to x = -3$$

Graphs A and C have roots 2 and -3.

Now, simplify the equation of the function:

$$p(x) = (x - 2)(x + 3) = x^2 + x - 6.$$

The coefficient of the leading term in the polynomial function is positive, so the end behavior of the function is $+\infty$ when $x \to \pm\infty$. Graph A is upward and thus the best represents the polynomial $p(x)$.

13) Choice A is correct

The easiest way to solve this one is to plug the answers into the equation.

When you do this, you will see the only time $x = x^{-6}$ is when $x = 1$ or $x = 0$.

Only $x = 1$ is provided in the choices.

14) Choice D is correct

The value of x of the vertex in the equation of a quadratic in standard form is: $x = \frac{-b}{2a}$. (The standard equation of a quadratic is: $ax^2 + bx + c = 0$)

Let's find the vertex of each choice provided:

A. $y = 3x^2 - 3$ The vertex is: $(0, -3)$

B. $y = -3x^2 + 3$ The vertex is: $(0, 3)$

C. $y = x^2 + 3x - 3$ The vertex is: $(\frac{-3}{2}, \frac{-21}{4})$

D. $y = 4(x - 3)^2 - 3$

The vertex form of a parabola equation is in the form of $y = a(x - h)^2 + k$, where (h, k) is the vertex. Then $h = 3$ and $k = -3$. (This is the answer)

15) Choice D is correct

$$m^{\frac{1}{2}} n^{-2} m^4 n^{\frac{2}{3}} \rightarrow m^{\frac{1}{2}} . m^4 = m^{\frac{1}{2}+4} = m^{\frac{9}{2}}, \quad n^{-2} . n^{\frac{2}{3}} = n^{-2+\frac{2}{3}} = n^{-\frac{4}{3}} = \frac{1}{n^{\frac{4}{3}}},$$

$$m^{\frac{9}{2}} . \frac{1}{n^{\frac{4}{3}}} = \frac{m^{\frac{9}{2}}}{n^{\frac{4}{3}}}$$

16) Choice D is correct

From the content of the question, we know that the starting point is 0 with the value of $400 (Corresponds to the ordered pair $(0, 400)$.). So far, one of the choices of either A or D can be the correct answer. She can work a maximum of 54 hours per week. Then the endpoint of the domain is $54 - 30 = 24$. Because the editor earns $15 per hour worked over 30 hours, the final income is $15 \times 24 + 400 = 760$. It is the point at the coordinate $(24, 760)$. Therefore, choice D is the answer.

17) Choice C is correct

The choices are the graphs of quadratic functions. If the range of a quadratic function is less than a number, it means that the function has a maximum value. Then, either graph C or D is the answer. The maximum value is -1, then the graph C is the correct answer.

18) Choice B is correct

Multiply by the conjugate: $\frac{\sqrt{5}+1}{\sqrt{5}+1}$

$$\frac{8}{\sqrt{5}-1} \times \frac{\sqrt{5}+1}{\sqrt{5}+1} = \frac{8(\sqrt{5}+1)}{4} = 2(\sqrt{5}+1)$$

19) Choice C is correct

The x −intercept is equal to 32. Actually, 32 is the root of the equation corresponding to the graph. Evaluate the root of the equation of each choice.

A. $y = 0 \rightarrow \frac{5}{9}x = 0 \rightarrow x = 0$

B. $y = 0 \rightarrow \frac{9}{5}x + 32 = 0 \rightarrow \frac{9}{5}x = -32 \rightarrow x = -\frac{160}{9}$

C. $y = 0 \rightarrow \frac{5}{9}(x - 32) = 0 \rightarrow x - 32 = 0 \rightarrow x = 32$

D. $y = 0 \rightarrow \frac{9}{5}(x - 32) = 0 \rightarrow x - 32 = 0 \rightarrow x = 32$

Therefore, one of the choices C or D is the answer. To determine the correct model, substitute another point on the graph in the possible equations. For example, we check point $x = 104$. So,

C. $x = 104 \rightarrow \frac{5}{9}(104 - 32) = \frac{5}{9}(72) = 5(8) = 40$

D. $x = 104 \rightarrow \frac{9}{5}(104 - 32) = \frac{9}{5}(72) = \frac{648}{5} = 129.6$

Thus, the choice C is the best representation of the graph.

20) Choice B is correct

Let x be the number of new shoes the team can purchase. Therefore, the team can purchase $120x$. The team had $\$20,000$ and spent $\$14,000$. Now the team can spend on new shoes $\$6,000$ at most. Now, write the inequality: $120x + 14,000 \leq 20,000$

21) Choice A is correct

The amount of money that Jack earns for one hour: $\frac{\$616}{44} = \$14$

The number of additional hours that he works to make enough money is: $\frac{\$826-\$616}{1.5\times\$14} = 10$

The number of total hours is: $44 + 10 = 54$

22) Choice A is correct

First, determine the common factors from each part of the expression: $35r^2 = 7 \times 5 \times r \times r$ and $28r = 7 \times 2 \times 2 \times r$. The common factors are 7 and r. Now, Rewrite as follow:

$$35r^2 - 28r = 7r(5r) - 7r(4)$$

Factor in $7r$: It means that $7r(5r) - 7r(4) = 7r(5r - 4)$. Therefore,

$$35r^2 - 28r = 7r(5r - 4).$$

23) Choice B is correct

By looking at the choices, you can see that the expected model is a quadratic function. After the rocket is launched, the height first increases and then decreases. Therefore, the suitable model has a maximum value. So, the coefficient of the leading term is negative. Either choice B or C is true. Now, substitute some points of the left column on the functions of B and C, then compare the corresponding values to the value of the right column.

Time (seconds)	Height (meters) for Choice C, y	Height (meters) for Choice B, y
5	690	750
10	1200	1290
15	1500	1620
20	1590	1740
25	1470	1650
30	1140	1350
35	600	840

The choice B is the best answer.

Keystone Algebra I Practice Tests 3 Explanations
Section 2

24) The value of m is 2

Let the equation be $P(x) = 6x^2 + 4x - 10$. Factor 2 from the equation: $6x^2 + 4x - 10 = 2(3x^2 + 2x - 5)$. We just need to factor the expression $Q(x) = 3x^2 + 2x - 5$. First, find the roots of the equation $3x^2 + 2x - 5 = 0$ by evaluating the discriminant expression $\Delta = b^2 - 4ac$ of the quadratic equation as $ax^2 + bx + c = 0$. So, we have:

$$\Delta = (2)^2 - 4(3)(-5) = 4 + 60 = 64 \rightarrow \Delta > 0$$

Use the quadratic formula: $x_{1,2} = \frac{-b \pm \sqrt{\Delta}}{2a}$. Therefore, the zeros of the equation $3x^2 + 2x - 5 = 0$ are $x_1 = \frac{-2+\sqrt{64}}{2(3)} = \frac{-2+8}{6} = 1$ or $x_2 = \frac{-2-\sqrt{64}}{2(3)} = \frac{-2-8}{6} = -\frac{10}{6} = -\frac{5}{3}$.

Then, the equation $Q(x) = 0$, can be written in factored form as

$$(x - 1)\left(x + \frac{5}{3}\right) = 0$$

Multiply both sides of the equation by 3:

$$3 \times (x - 1)\left(x + \frac{5}{3}\right) = 3 \times 0 \rightarrow (x - 1)(3x + 5) = 0$$

It's equivalent to the equation $3x^2 + 2x - 5 = 0$. Now, to obtain the expression $P(x)$, multiply both sides of the expression $Q(x)$ by 2. Thus,

$$P(x) = 2Q(x) \rightarrow P(x) = 2(x - 1)(3x + 5) \rightarrow P(x) = (2x - 2)(3x + 5)$$

Compare the resulting factor with the factored expression in the content of the question:

$$(2x - 2)(3x + 5) = (2x - m)(3x + 5)$$

You can see that the value of m is 2.

25) The negative solution is -5

Simplify, $\frac{2x^2}{5} - 10 = 0$. First, multiply both sides of the equation by 5:

$$5 \times \left(\frac{2x^2}{5} - 10\right) = 5 \times 0 \rightarrow 5 \times \frac{2x^2}{5} - 5 \times 10 = 0 \rightarrow 2x^2 - 50 = 0.$$

Add 50 to both sides: $2x^2 - 50 + 50 = 0 + 50 \rightarrow 2x^2 = 50$. Now, divide both sides by 2. Then, $2x^2 \div 2 = 50 \div 2 \rightarrow x^2 = 25$. Therefore, $x = \pm5$.

26) The value of $f(8)$ is -1

To find the value of $f(8)$, make $x^3 = 8$. Then,

$$x^3 = 8 \rightarrow x = 2$$

Finally, $x = 2 \rightarrow f(2^3) = 2(2) - 5 = -1 \rightarrow f(8) = -1$.

27) The correct answer is 1

First, find a common denominator for x and $\frac{3x}{2-x}$. It's $2 - x$. Then:

$$\frac{3x}{2-x} - x = \frac{3x}{2-x} - \frac{x(2-x)}{2-x} = \frac{3x - 2x + x^2}{2-x} = \frac{x^2 + x}{2-x}.$$

Now, multiply both sides of equation $1 = \frac{x^2+x}{2-x}$ by $2 - x$. Then:

$$(2 - x) \times 2 = (2 - x) \times \frac{x^2+x}{2-x}.$$

Rewrite the expression: $4 - 2x = x^2 + x$. Simplify as $x^2 + 3x - 4 = 0$.

Now, factor it. To factorize this quadratic equation, we need to find two numbers that multiply to -4 (the constant term) and add up to 3 (the coefficient of the x term).

These numbers are 4 and -1 because 4 multiplied by -1 equals -4 and 4 plus -1 equals 3.

So, the factored form of the equation is: $(x + 4)(x - 1) = 0$

Setting each factor equal to zero gives the solutions: $(x + 4) = 0 \Rightarrow x = -4$ and

$$(x - 1) = 0 \Rightarrow x = 1$$

So, the solutions to the equation are $x = -4$ and $x = 1$.

Only $x = 1$ is a positive solution.

Keystone Algebra I Practice Tests 4 Explanations
Section 1

1) Choice C is correct

According to the given graph of the function f, first, the graph f goes 3 units to the left, and the graph of $k(x) = f(x + 3)$ is obtained as follows:

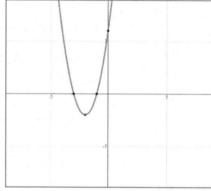

Now, by shifting 2 units to the up, the graph of $g(x) = f(x + 3) + 2$ is obtained.

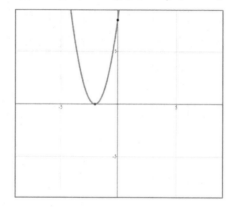

2) Choice C is correct

$$6x^2 - 4x - 10 = 2(x + 1)(3x - 5)$$

3) Choice A is correct

Use the correlation coefficient formula:

$$r = \frac{\sum(x_i - \bar{x})(y_i - \bar{y})}{\sqrt{\sum(x_i - \bar{x})^2(y_i - \bar{y})^2}}$$

Where $\bar{x}$ and $\bar{y}$ are the means of the values of the x and y variables. Evaluate the mean of the heights, x_i, and the lengths, y_i. Then, the mean of the heights is $\bar{x} = 37.8$ and the lengths is $\bar{y} = 28.9$. According to the following table, we have:

$$r = \frac{\sum(x_i - \bar{x})(y_i - \bar{y})}{\sqrt{\sum(x_i - \bar{x})^2(y_i - \bar{y})^2}} = \frac{725.8}{\sqrt{7355558.84}} \cong 0.27$$

Height, x_i	36	70	16	30	10	87	53	28	9	39
Length, y_i	21	20	32	11	18	45	38	23	42	39
$x_i - \bar{x}$	−1.8	32.2	−21.8	−7.8	−27.8	49.2	15.2	−9.8	−28.8	1.2
$y_i - \bar{y}$	−7.9	−8.9	3.1	−17.9	−10.9	16.1	9.1	−5.9	13.1	10.1

The correlation coefficient is positive. So, it's a weak positive correction.

4) Choice A is correct

Remember that an exponential function has one horizontal asymptote. The horizontal asymptote of the exponential function is the horizontal line (the choices A or B can be the suitable answer) that becomes close to it for large negative or positive x. Clearly, the above exponential function graph gets close to the line M for the large positive x.

5) Choice A is correct

Check the transformation properties of the functions. The graph of function $k(x) = f(x) + (-4)$ shifted up by -4 units. Note that the graph of function $h(x) = f\left(\frac{1}{2}x\right)$, is stretched horizontally relate to $f(x)$, and the graph of $l(x) = f(-x)$, is symmetric to the function $f(x)$ with respect to the x −axis. The combination of these functions produces the function $g(x) = f\left(-\frac{x}{2}\right) - 4$.

A is true. The graph of g is a reflection of the graph of f across the x −axis. B, C, and D are not correct.

6) Choice D is correct

Choice D is the correct answer because $(x^y)^z$ is the same as $x^{y \times z}$.

7) Choice A is correct

Consider the variable part to be $a(a + b)^2$, then this expression has two like terms with coefficients -15 and 23. Then: $-15a(a + b)^2 + 23a(a + b)^2 = 8a(a + b)^2$.

8) Choice C is correct

First, graph the equation $y = -3x$. So, we have:

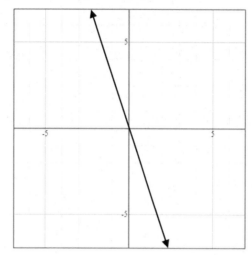

Since the sign of the inequality is greater than $>$, then the corresponding graph has a dashed line. That is, the choice B or C is the possible answer. Now, substitute an arbitrary point on the coordinate plane of one side of the graph in the given inequality like $(1,0)$. So,

$$(1,0) \rightarrow -3(1) = -3 < 0. \text{ It is true.}$$

Choice C is the correct answer.

9) Choice D is correct

Check the correctness of each statement:

A. Plug the point $(-1,2)$ in the function and evaluate: $f(-1) = 4(1.25)^{-1} = 3.2 \neq 2$.

B. Exponential functions in standard form $y = a(b)^x$ have a horizontal asymptote to the equation of $y = 0$.

C. The function $f(x)$ does not intersect the $x-$axis. Because the equation $f(x) = 0$ has no solution.

D. The base of the exponential function $f(x) = 4(1.25)^x$ is greater than 1, so it is increasing.

10) Choice A is correct

Remember that the $y-$intercept is the point where the graph intersects the $y-$axis. Then the first component of the ordered pair of corresponding to the $y-$intercept is zero. One of the choices is A or C. The graph intersects the $y-$axis on the upside of the $y-$axis. So, the second component of the ordered pair is positive. That is, the choice A is the answer.

11) Choice C is correct

A. The given graph cuts the $y-$axis in one point with the coordinate $(0,1)$, then the $y-$intercept is 1. Then, this choice is NOT true!

B. To find the domain of the graph of the function, draw the image of the graph on the $x-$axis.

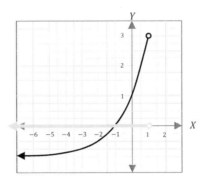

Therefore, the inequality $-\infty < x < 1$ is the solution set of the domain of the part of the graph. It means that the interval $(-\infty, 1)$. This interval is NOT equal to the interval $(-\infty, 1]$.

C. The image of the graph on the $y-$axis is as follows:

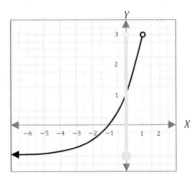

Therefore, the interval $(-1,3)$ is the range of the graph. It's the correct answer.

D. Choice D is NOT true! Because the graph cuts the $x-$axis in the point $(-1,0)$, then the $x-$intercept is -1.

12) Choice D is correct

$x^2 = 121 \rightarrow x = 11$ (Positive value) Or $x = -11$ (negative value)

Since x is positive, then: $f(121) = f(11^2) = 3(11) + 4 = 33 + 4 = 37$.

13) Choice D is correct

$2x^2 - 11x + 8 = -3x + 18 \rightarrow 2x^2 - 11x + 3x + 8 - 18 = 0 \rightarrow 2x^2 - 8x - 10 = 0$

$\rightarrow 2(x^2 - 4x - 5) = 0 \rightarrow$ Divide both sides by 2. Then: $x^2 - 4x - 5 = 0$, Find the factors of the quadratic equation. $\rightarrow (x - 5)(x + 1) = 0 \rightarrow x = 5 \qquad$ or $\qquad x = -1$

$a > b$, then: $a = 5$ and $b = -1 \qquad \dfrac{a}{b} = \dfrac{5}{-1} = -5$

14) Choice B is correct

We know that the graph $y = f(x) + k; k > 0$, is shifted k units up of the graph $y = f(x)$, and if $k < 0$, is shifted k units down. Then, $y = x^2 - 2$ is shifted 2 units down of the graph $y = x^2$.

15) Choice A is correct

Perfect cube formula: $(a + b)^3 = a^3 + 3a^2b + 3ab^2 + b^3$. Then:

$$(3x + 2)^3 = (3x)^3 + 3.(3x)^2.2 + 3.(3x).2^2 + 2^3 = 27x^3 + 54x^2 + 36x + 8$$

16) Choice C is correct

Plug in the values of x and y of the point $(2, 12)$ in the equation of the quadratic function. Then:

$$12 = a(2)^2 + 5(2) + 10 \rightarrow 12 = 4a + 10 + 10 \rightarrow 12 = 4a + 20$$

$$\rightarrow 4a = 12 - 20 = -8 \rightarrow a = \frac{-8}{4} = -2 \rightarrow a^2 = (-2)^2 = 4$$

17) Choice B is correct

Since the vertex of a quadratic function is the highest/lowest point on the graph. So, the vertex of this quadratic function is clearly an ordered pair with coordinates $(-2,5)$. Indicated in the graph below.

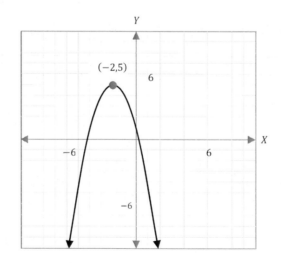

18) Choice A is correct

Use the polynomial identity: $(x - y)^2 = x^2 - 2xy + y^2$ for the part of the equation of function $(2 - 3x)^2$. Then:

$$(2 - 3x)^2 = (2)^2 - 2(2)(3x) + (3x)^2 = 4 - 12x + 9x^2.$$

Substitute the obtained expression in the equation of function and simplify.

$$2(2 - 3x)^2 - 7 = 2(4 - 12x + 9x^2) - 7 = 18x^2 - 24x + 1.$$

Therefore: $f(x) = 18x^2 - 24x + 1.$

19) Choice C is correct

$\begin{cases} \frac{-x}{2} + \frac{y}{4} = 1 \\ \frac{-5y}{6} + 2x = 4 \end{cases}$ → Multiply the top equation by 4. Then,

$\begin{cases} -2x + y = 4 \\ \frac{-5y}{6} + 2x = 4 \end{cases}$ → Add two equations. $\frac{1}{6}y = 8 \rightarrow y = 48$, plug in the value of y into the first

equation $x = 22$

20) Choice D is correct

The description $8 + 2x$ is 16 more than 20 can be written as the equation $8 + 2x = 16 + 20$, which is equivalent to $8 + 2x = 36$. Subtracting 8 from each side of $8 + 2x = 36$ gives

$2x = 28$. Since $6x$ is 3 times $2x$, multiplying both sides of $2x = 28$ by 3 gives $6x = 84$.

21) Choice B is correct

For each option, choose a point in the solution part and check it on both inequalities.

$y \leq x + 4, 2x + y \leq -4$

A. Let's choose this point $(0, 5)$ $5 \leq 0 + 4$, That's not true.

B. Point $(-4, -4)$ is in the solution section. Let's check the point in both inequalities.

$-4 \leq -4 + 4$, It works

$2(-4) + (-4) \leq -4 \Rightarrow -12 \leq -4$, it works (this point works in both inequalities)

C. Let's choose this point $(0, 0)$ $0 \leq 0 + 4$, It works, $2(0) + (0) \leq -4$, That's not true!

D. Let's choose this point $(-5, 0)$, $0 \leq -5 + 4$, That's not true!

Only choice B represents both inequalities.

22) Choice D is correct

First, use this polynomial identity: $(x + y)(x - y) = x^2 - y^2$. Then:

$$4x^2 - 81 = (2x + 9)(2x - 9)$$

By factoring the value of 2 from each parenthesis as $(2x + 9) = 2(x + 4.5)$ and $(2x - 9) = 2(x - 4.5)$, we have:

$$4x^2 - 81 = 4(x + 4.5)(x - 4.5)$$

23) Choice B is correct

Plug in each pair of numbers in the equation:

    A. $(2, 1)$: $2(2) + 4(1) = 8$ This is NOT true.

    B. $(-1, 2)$: $2(-1) + 4(2) = 6$ This is true.

    C. $(-2, 2)$: $2(-2) + 4(2) = 4$ This is NOT true.

    D. $(2, 2)$: $2(2) + 4(2) = 12$ This is NOT true.

Keystone Algebra I Practice Tests 4 Explanations
Section 2

24) The rate of change is 9

Since the relationship is linear, the rate of change is equal to the slope of the line passing through the table points. Use the slope formula of the line passing through two points (x_1, y_1) and (x_2, y_2) in the form of $m = \frac{y_2 - y_1}{x_2 - x_1}$. Consider arbitrary points like $(0, 72)$ and $(91, 891)$ from the given table. Therefore,

$$\text{Rate of change} = \frac{891 - 72}{91 - 0} = \frac{819}{91} = 9.$$

25) The zeros of function g is -3

First, write the equation of the line passing through the two points (marked) on the graph. For the two points $(x_1 y_1)$ and $(x_2 y_2)$, use the formula

$$y - y_1 = m(x - x_1)$$

Where the slope is $m = \frac{y_2 - y_1}{x_2 - x_1}$. For two points $(-6, -6)$ and $(1, 8)$ the slope is $m = \frac{8 - (-6)}{1 - (-6)} = \frac{14}{7} = 2$. Then:

$$y - 8 = 2(x - 1) \rightarrow y = 2x + 6$$

To find the zero of the function g put $y = 0$ and solve this equation

$$2x + 6 = 0 \rightarrow 2x = -6 \rightarrow x = -3$$

The zero of function g is -3.

26) The value of b is 42

Note that two variables are directly proportional whenever one amount increases, another amount increases at the same rate. First, evaluate the rate of b to a. So,

$$b = ra \rightarrow r = \frac{b}{a} \rightarrow r = \frac{7}{2.5} = 2.8$$

Now, put the rate of b to a equal to $r = 2.8$. Then, $b = 2.8a \rightarrow 2.8 \times 15 = 42$.

27) The value of k is -2

Notice that for the function $g(x)$, if $k > 0$ then $f(x) = g(x) + k$ shifted to the up by $|k|$ units, and if $k < 0$ the function $f(x) = g(x) + k$ shifted to the down by $|k|$ units. The graph of the function $g(x) = x^2$ is as follow:

If $g(x)$ is shifted down by 2 units, the graph of $f(x)$ is obtained. Therefore, the value of k is -2 and the corresponding equation is $f(x) = g(x) - 2 \rightarrow f(x) = x^2 - 2$.

Keystone Algebra I Practice Tests 5 Explanations
Section 1

1) Choice A is correct

Find the factor of the number 324.

$$324 = 3 \times 3 \times 3 \times 3 \times 2 \times 2 = 3^3 \times 3 \times 2 \times 2.$$

Use the radical rules: $\sqrt[n]{a^n} = a$ and $\sqrt[n]{a \times b} = \sqrt[n]{a} \times \sqrt[n]{b}$. Then:

$$\sqrt[3]{324} = \sqrt[3]{3 \times 3 \times 3 \times 3 \times 2 \times 2} = \sqrt[3]{3^3 \times 3 \times 2 \times 2} = \sqrt[3]{3^3} \times \sqrt[3]{3 \times 2 \times 2} = 3\sqrt[3]{12}.$$

2) Choice B is correct

Multiply two exponents: $(x^6)^{\frac{7}{8}} = x^{6 \times \frac{7}{8}} = x^{\frac{42}{8}} = x^{\frac{21}{4}}$.

3) Choice B is correct

To generate the terms of the recursive sequence, put the previous terms in the explicit formula and calculate. Plug in $n = 3$ into the explicit formula $a_n = 3a_{n-1} - a_{n-2}$. So, $a_3 = 3a_{3-1} - a_{3-2} \rightarrow a_3 = 3a_2 - a_1$

Then, substitute $a_1 = 3$ and $a_2 = 2$ into the resulting formula. Therefore,

$$a_3 = 3(2) - 3 = 6 - 3 = 3 \rightarrow a_3 = 3$$

Calculate the next terms in a similar way.

$$n = 4 \rightarrow a_4 = 3a_3 - a_2 \rightarrow \begin{matrix} a_3 = 3 \\ a_2 = 2 \end{matrix} \rightarrow a_4 = 3(3) - 2 = 7 \rightarrow a_4 = 7$$

$$n = 5 \rightarrow a_5 = 3a_4 - a_3 \rightarrow \begin{matrix} a_4 = 7 \\ a_3 = 3 \end{matrix} \rightarrow a_5 = 3(7) - 3 = 18 \rightarrow a_4 = 18$$

It is the first five terms of this sequence: 3, 2, 3, 7, 18.

4) Choice D is correct

Use distributive property: $2x(5 + 3y + 2x + 4z) = 10x + 6xy + 4x^2 + 8xz$.

5) Choice A is correct

The graph of quadratic parent function $f(x) = x^2$ is

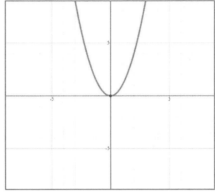

We know that the function $g(x) = f(x - h)$ if $h > 0$, shifted to the right, and if $h < 0$, shifted to the left. So, the graph of function $g(x) = f(x + 4) \rightarrow g(x) = f\big(x - (-4)\big)$ goes 4 units to the left as follow:

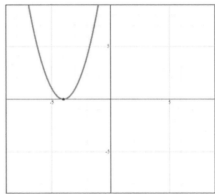

On the other hand, for the function $l(x) = f(x) + k$ if $k > 0$, shifted to the up, and if $k < 0$, shifted to the down. So, the graph of function $k(x) = g(x) - 5 \rightarrow k(x) = g(x) + (-5)$ shifted 5 units to the down. So, we have:

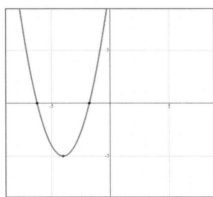

Therefore, the choice A is the correct answer.

6) Choice A is correct

Let y be Anna's age: $5y + 3 = x \rightarrow 5y = x - 3 \rightarrow y = \frac{x-3}{5}$

7) Choice D is correct

Remember that the range of an exponential function is all real numbers greater than zero. That is, $0 \le y$. In addition, the function is going down and the values before 1850 are not in the range of the graph. So, the range of f is the inequality $0 < y \le 850$.

8) Choice B is correct

Find the factor of the numbers:

$8 = 4 \times 2 = 2^2 \times 2$

$50 = 25 \times 2 = 5^2 \times 2$

$72 = 36 \times 2 = 6^2 \times 2$

Now use the radical rule: $\sqrt[n]{a^n} = a$

Finally: $\sqrt{8} - \sqrt{50} + \sqrt{72} = \sqrt{2^2 \times 2} - \sqrt{5^2 \times 2} + \sqrt{6^2 \times 2} = 2\sqrt{2} - 5\sqrt{2} + 6\sqrt{2} = 3\sqrt{2}.$

9) Choice C is correct

Using this identity: $(x + a)(x + b) = x^2 + (a + b)x + ab$. Now, we have:

$$x^2 - 2x - 15 = x^2 + \left(3 + (-5)\right)x + \left(3 \times (-5)\right) \rightarrow g(x) = (x + 3)(x - 5).$$

Then, the factors of g are $(x + 3)$ and $(x - 5)$. Evaluate $g(x) = 0$. Therefore:

$$(x + 3)(x - 5) = 0 \rightarrow x = -3 \text{ and } x = 5.$$

10) Choice C is correct

First, write the equation in slope-intercept form. Add $2x$ to both sides to get $6y = 2x + 24$. Now divide both sides by 6 to get $y = \frac{1}{3}x + 4$. The slope of this line is $\frac{1}{3}$, so any line that also has a slope of $\frac{1}{3}$ would be parallel to it. Only choice C has a slope of $\frac{1}{3}$.

11) Choice C is correct

Adding 6 to each side of the inequality $4n - 3 \ge 1$ yields the inequality $4n + 3 \ge 7$. Therefore, the least possible value of $4n + 3$ is 7.

12) Choice C is correct

Substitute a few points of the graph into the equations and check which equation passes through the points. First, evaluate the starting point $(0,0)$. Therefore,

A. $0 = -9(0)^2 - 72(0)$
B. $0 \neq -9(0)^2 - 144(0) - 576 = -576$
C. $0 = -9(0)^2 + 72(0)$
D. $0 = -9(0)^2 + 144(0) - 576 = -576$

Now, evaluate the vertex point $(4,144)$ for the remaining equations. So,

A. $144 \neq -9(4)^2 - 72(4) = -144 - 288 = -432$
C. $144 = -9(4)^2 + 72(4) = -144 + 288$

Finally, the choice C is the correct answer.

13) Choice B is correct

$$(x - 2)^3 = 27 \rightarrow x - 2 = 3 \rightarrow x = 5 \rightarrow (x - 6)(x - 4) = (5 - 6)(5 - 4)$$

$$= (-1)(1) = -1$$

14) Choice D is correct

Rewrite the expression as $9 - 49x^2$. Use the following polynomial identity:

$$x^2 - y^2 = (x + y)(x - y).$$

Then: $9 - 49x^2 = (3 + 7x)(3 - 7x)$.

15) Choice D is correct

To find the slope of a line, find two points on the line and use the slope formula: $m = \frac{y_2 - y_1}{x_2 - x_1}$

Let's choose these two points: $(-4, 0)$ and $(0, -2)$. The slope of the line is:

$$m = \frac{y_2 - y_1}{x_2 - x_1} = \frac{-2 - 0}{0 - (-4)} = \frac{-2}{4} = -\frac{1}{2}$$

The slope of the line is $-\frac{1}{2}$.

16) Choice B is correct

To find the y-intercept, rearrange the equation $3x - 6y = 24$ so that y is isolated: $-6y = 24 - 3x \rightarrow y = \frac{1}{2}x - 4$ so the y-intercept is -4.

To find the x-intercept, arrange the equation $3x - 6y = 24$ so that x is isolated: $3x = 6y + 24 \rightarrow x = 2y + 8$

Using the point-slope formula, we see that the x-intercept is 8.

17) Choice B is correct

First, factor the function: $(x - 4)(x - 3)$. To find the zeros, $f(x)$ should be zero:

$f(x) = (x - 4)(x - 3) = 0$, Therefore, the zeros are, $(x - 4) = 0 \Rightarrow x = 4$,

$(x - 3) = 0 \Rightarrow x = 3$

18) Choice C is correct

$0.35 per minute to use the car. This per-minute rate can be converted to the hourly rate using the conversion 1 hour = 60 minutes, as shown below.

$$\frac{0.35}{minute} \times \frac{60\ minutes}{1\ hours} = \frac{\$(0.35 \times 60)}{hour}$$

Thus, the car costs $\$(0.35 \times 60)$ per hour.

Therefore, the cost c, in dollars, for h hours of use is $c = (0.35 \times 60)h$,

Which is equivalent to $c = 0.35(60h)$.

19) Choice A is correct

The function $f(x)$ is undefined when the denominator of $\frac{1}{(x-3)^2+4(x-3)+4}$ is equal to zero. The expression $(x - 3)^2 + 4(x - 3) + 4$ is a perfect square.

$(x - 3)^2 + 4(x - 3) + 4 = ((x - 3) + 2)^2$ which can be rewritten as $(x - 1)^2$. The expression $(x - 1)^2$ is equal to zero if and only if $x = 1$. Therefore, the value of x for which $f(x)$ is undefined is 1.

20) Choice B is correct

Simple interest (y) is calculated by multiplying the initial deposit (p), by the interest rate (r), and time (t). $360 = 240 \times 0.1 \times t \rightarrow 360 = 24t \rightarrow t = \frac{360}{24} = 15$

So, it takes 15 years to get $360 with an investment of $240.

21) Choice D is correct

Five years ago, Amy was three times as old as Mike. Mike is 10 years now. Therefore, 5 years ago Mike was 5 years. Five years ago, Amy was: $A = 3 \times 5 = 15$, Now Amy is 20 years old: $15 + 5 = 20$

22) Choice C is correct

The graph is a quadratic function. Since the domain of a quadratic function is all real numbers then the choice C is the answer.

23) Choice D is correct

The solution set of $x \leq 1$ represents all the values of x that are less than or equal to 1. To graph this inequality, we can draw a vertical line at $x = 1$ and shade the region to the left of the line since those are the values of x that satisfy the inequality.

Keystone Algebra I Practice Tests 5 Explanations
Section 2

24) The y −intercept is 42

In order to find the y −intercept, you must put the value of the variable x in the equation of the function $k(x)$ equal to zero. Therefore,

$$x = 0 \rightarrow k(0) = 42\left(\frac{4}{5}\right)^0 = 42.$$

25) The value of x is -3

First, multiply $6x - 7$ by -1. Then, $-(6x - 7) = -6x + 7$. Similarly, we have for $5(8 + x)$: $5(8 + x) = 40 + 5x$. Substitute the recent expression in the equation as

$$-(6x - 7) = 5(8 + x) \rightarrow -6x + 7 = 40 + 5x.$$

Subtract 7 from both sides: $-6x + 7 - 7 = 40 + 5x - 7 \rightarrow -6x = 33 + 5x$. Then, subtract $5x$ from both sides of the equation: $-6x - 5x = 33 + 5x - 5x \rightarrow -11x = 33$. Now, divide both sides of $-11x = 33$ by -11. Therefore, $x = -3$.

26) The value of $n - m$ is -9

For the expression $(xy^{-2})^3$, use the exponential rule as $(xy)^a = x^a \times y^a$. Then:

$$(xy^{-2})^3 = x^3 \times (y^{-2})^3$$

In this case, by using the rule $(x^a)^b = x^{a \times b}$, we have: $(y^{-2})^3 = y^{-2 \times 3} = y^{-6}$. Substitute the expression in the resulting expression from $(xy^{-2})^3$:

$$(xy^{-2})^3 = x^3 y^{-6}$$

Consider to the rule: $\left(\frac{a}{b}\right)^c = \frac{a^c}{b^c}$ for the expression $\left(\frac{y}{x}\right)^9$, then: $\left(\frac{y}{x}\right)^9 = \frac{y^9}{x^9} = y^9 x^{-9}$. Substitute $y^9 x^{-9}$ and $x^3 y^{-6}$ in the content expression: $(xy^{-2})^3 \left(\frac{y}{x}\right)^9 = x^3 y^{-6} y^9 x^{-9}$. Arrange the terms to have the same base in the expression $x^3 y^{-6} y^9 x^{-9}$ to form $x^3 x^{-9} y^{-6} y^9$. According to the exponential rule: $x^a \times x^b = x^{a+b}$. Thus, $x^3 x^{-9} y^{-6} y^9 = x^{3-9} y^{-6+9} = x^{-6} y^3$.

Put $x^n y^m = x^{-6} y^3$. The values n and m are -6 and 3, respectively. Therefore,

$$n - m = -6 - (3) = -9.$$

27) The value of y is 10

Note that two variables are directly proportional whenever one amount increases, another amount increases at the same rate. Evaluate the rate of y to x. So,

$$y = rx \rightarrow r = \frac{y}{x} \rightarrow r = \frac{4}{7}$$

Put the rate of y to x equal to $r = \frac{4}{7}$. Then,

$$\frac{4}{7} = \frac{y}{17.5} \rightarrow 17.5 \times \left(\frac{4}{7}\right) = 17.5 \times \left(\frac{y}{17.5}\right) \rightarrow y = \frac{17.5 \times 4}{7} = 10.$$

Keystone Algebra I Practice Tests 6 Explanations
Section 1

1) Choice C is correct

Based on the problem information, the late fee for overdue books is $0.2 per day per book. The late fee for 5 overdue books is $1 per day: $5 \times 0.2 = 1$. Therefore, for each late day, $1 will be added to the late fee. The late fee equation for five overdue books is linear and is in the form of $y = x$.

Choice D is false because the maximum late fee is $4.00 per book, which equals $20 for 5 books. Then, the range of the graph related to the late fee of these 5 books is not more than $20.

The choice C is a suitable answer.

2) Choice B is correct

When the discus launched from the ground, its height is 0 feet. Substituting 0 for h in $h = -10t^2 + 44t$ gives $0 = -10t^2 + 44t$, which can be rewritten as $0 = t(-10t + 44)$. Thus, the possible values of t are $t = 0$ and $t = \frac{44}{10} = 4.4$. The time $t = 0$ seconds corresponds to the time the discus is launched from the ground, and the time $t = 4.4$ seconds corresponds to the time after launch that the discus hits the ground, so the discus returns to the ground 4.4 seconds after it is launched.

Choice A, C, and D are incorrect and could arise from conceptual or computation errors while solving $0 = -10t^2 + 44t$ for t.

3) Choice C is correct

To solve for the value of x, we substitute $y = -6$ in the equation $y = -\frac{3}{4}x - 1$ and solve for x:
$-6 = -\frac{3}{4}x - 1$.

Adding 1 to both sides, we get: $-5 = -\frac{3}{4}x$.

Multiplying both sides by $-\frac{4}{3}$, we get: $\left(-\frac{4}{3}\right)(-5) = x$.

Simplifying, we get $x = \frac{20}{3}$.

Therefore, the value of x when $y = -6$ is $\frac{20}{3}$.

4) Choice A is correct

Since none of the given points in the set $\{(2,5)(0,1)(4,17)(-1,-1)(-3,1)\}$ are related by any exponent or root, we can eliminate options B, C, and D, leaving only option A as a possible parent function. Therefore, the parent function of f is $y = x$.

5) Choice C is correct

Substituting 0 for x in the given equation yields $3(0)^2 + 6(0) + 2 = 2$. Therefore, the graph of the given equation passes through the point $(0, 2)$, which is the y-intercept of the graph. The right-hand side of the given equation, $y = 3x^2 + 6x + 2$, displays the constant 2, which directly corresponds to the y-coordinate of the y-intercept of the graph of this equation in the xy-plane.

6) Choice B is correct

To find the x −intercepts of the graph of the quadratic function, we need to set $h(x) = 0$ and solve for x.

For the function $h(x) = -2x^2 + 2x + 4$, we have:

$-2x^2 + 2x + 4 = 0$.

Dividing both sides by -2, we get:

$x^2 - x - 2 = 0$.

To solve this quadratic equation, we can use the quadratic formula:

$x = \frac{(-b \pm \sqrt{b^2 - 4ac})}{2a}$, where $a = 1$, $b = -1$, and $c = -2$.

Plugging in these values, we get:

$x = \frac{\left(-(-1) \pm \sqrt{(-1)^2 - 4(1)(-2)}\right)}{2(1)} = \frac{1 \pm \sqrt{9}}{2}$

So, the x −intercepts of the graph of the function $h(x)$ are:

$(2,0)$ and $(-1,0)$.

Therefore, the answer is B.

7) Choice B is correct

If $y = f(x)$, then we can substitute $x = 12$ to find the value of y: $y = f(12)$ but we're given that $f(12) = 6$, so $y = 6$ Therefore, the answer is B.

8) Choice D is correct

To solve the problem, model the data in the table. Let y be the total number of blocks carried and x be the number of times the lifter is used.

We know that the lift is loaded with the same number of blocks every time it is used, then the rate of change of the equation is constant and equal to the number of blocks each time the elevator is used. Therefore, the model is linear and has the slope m equal to the rate of change of this equation. The equation is in the form $y = mx$.

To find m, substitute one of the rows of the table in the equation and solve for m:

$(8,720) \rightarrow 720 = m \times 8 \rightarrow m = 90.$

Next, we get $y = 90x$. Finally, put $x = 11$ in the equation $y = 90x$ and get the value of y:

$y = 90 \times 11 = 990.$

9) Choice D is correct

To find the solution of this linear graph, write the equation of the line that passes through two points $(2,6)$ and $(-4,-3)$. The slope of the line passing through (x_1, y_1) and (x_2, y_2) is: $m = \frac{y_2 - y_1}{x_2 - x_1}$. So, for the points $(-4,-3)$ and $(2,6)$, we get:

$$m = \frac{6-(-3)}{2-(-4)} = \frac{3}{2}.$$

The slope of the line is $\frac{3}{2}$. Then, write the equation of the line passes through the point $(2,6)$ with the slope $m = \frac{3}{2}$:

$$y - 6 = \frac{3}{2}(x - 2) \rightarrow y - 6 = \frac{3}{2}x - 3 \rightarrow y = \frac{3}{2}x + 3.$$

Next, find the value of x when $y = 0$. Therefore, we have:

$\frac{3}{2}x + 3 = 0 \rightarrow \frac{3}{2}x = -3 \rightarrow x = -2.$

10) Choice D is correct

To find the answer, we need to calculate the difference between the number of apples the store ordered with the original function and the number of apples that were damaged when $x = 50$.

Using the original function, when $x = 50$: $f(50) = 150(50) + 25 = 7525.$

So, the store ordered 7525 apples if they ordered 50 crates using the original function.

Using the new function, when $x = 50$: $g(50) = 135(50) + 25 = 6775$.

So, the store ordered 6775 apples if they ordered 50 crates using the new function.

To find the difference, we subtract the number of apples the store ordered with the new function from the number they ordered with the original function: $7525 - 6775 = 750$.

Therefore, the store ordered 750 fewer apples available to sell if they ordered 50 crates using the new function.

11) Choice D is correct

The solution of $q(x) = 5$ is the intersection of the $q(x)$ and the horizontal line $y = 5$. We have drawn the intersection of these two equations on the graph below.

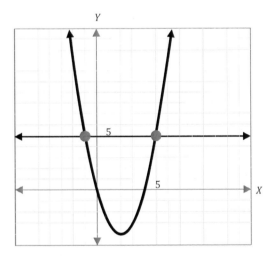

The solutions are -1 and 5.

12) Choice B is correct

The correct answer is B. The population of the city will reach 15,000 between 17 and 18 years from now.

The function given is a quadratic function of the form $p = at^2 + b$, where p represents the population of the city and t represents the time in years. The coefficient a is positive, which means that the graph of the function is a parabola that opens upward, indicating that the population is increasing.

To determine when the population reaches a certain value, we can set p equal to that value and solve for t. In this case, we want to know when the population reaches 15,000, so we set $p = 15,000$ and solve for t:

$$15,000 = 12,000 + 10t^2 \rightarrow 3,000 = 10t^2 \rightarrow t^2 = 300 \rightarrow t \cong 17.3 \text{ or } t \cong -17.3.$$

Since we're interested in the positive value of t, we can conclude that the population of the city will reach 15,000 between 17 and 18 years from now.

Option A is incorrect because the function is quadratic, so the rate of increase is not constant.

Option C is incorrect because the population of the city two years later from now is obtained by putting 2 in the equation $p = 12,000 + 10t^2$ and calculating $p = 12040$. The difference of this value from the initial value is 40.

Option D is incorrect because the function is a quadratic function with a positive leading coefficient, which means that the graph is a parabola that opens upward and does not have a decreasing portion from zero to $+\infty$.

13) Choice D is correct

All mapping points must be satisfied in corresponding representation. By checking the choices, we find that only choice D is correct.

14) Choice C is correct

To find the equation of a line in standard form, we need to rearrange it to the form $Ax + By = C$, where A, B, and C are constants.

We know that the line passes through point $(2,15)$ and has a slope of 1.5. Using the point-slope form of a line, we have:

$$y - y_1 = m(x - x_1) \rightarrow y - 15 = 1.5(x - 2).$$

Expanding and rearranging this equation, we get:

$$y - 15 = 1.5x - 3 \rightarrow y = 1.5x + 12.$$

To write this in standard form, we rearrange the terms:

$$-1.5x + y = 12.$$

Multiplying both sides by -2 to get integer coefficients, we have:

$$3x - 2y = -24.$$

So, the answer is C.

15) Choice B is correct

To find the vertex of the quadratic function $g(x) = 3x^2 + 4x + 2$, we need to use the formula $-\frac{b}{2a}$ to find the x −coordinate of the vertex, and then plug that value into the equation to find the corresponding y −coordinate.

In this case, $a = 3$ and $b = 4$, so the x −coordinate of the vertex is given by:

x −coordinate of vertex: $-\frac{b}{2a} = -\frac{4}{2(3)} = -\frac{4}{6} = -\frac{2}{3}$.

To find the y −coordinate of the vertex, we can plug in $x = -\frac{2}{3}$ into the equation for $g(x)$ and simplify:

y −coordinate of vertex: $g\left(-\frac{2}{3}\right) = 3\left(-\frac{2}{3}\right)^2 + 4\left(-\frac{2}{3}\right) + 2 = \frac{2}{3}$.

Therefore, the vertex of the graph of the quadratic function $g(x) = 3x^2 + 4x + 2$ is $\left(-\frac{2}{3}, \frac{2}{3}\right)$, which corresponds to answer choice B.

16) Choice C is correct

To solve the problem, first find the values of $g(-2)$ and $g(0)$ based on the table information:

$g(-2) = 4$ and $g(0) = 1$.

Next, substitute the values $g(-2) = 4$ and $g(0) = 1$ in the expression $1 - g\big(g(-2)\big) + 2g(0)$. Then:

$1 - g\big(g(-2)\big) + 2g(0) = 1 - g(4) + 2(1) = 3 - g(4)$.

Again, find the value of $g(4)$ from the table and put it in the obtained expression, we get:

$g(4) = 3 \rightarrow 3 - g(4) = 0$.

Therefore, the correct answer for the expression $1 - g\big(g(-2)\big) + 2g(0)$ is 0.

17) Choice B is correct

First, evaluate the slope of the line f. According to the graph, two points $(-2,0)$ and $(0,-2)$ are on the line f. So, the slope of the line f is -1. Since line g is less steep than line f, then the slope of line g must be less than -1 (Choices B or C are possible). Next, evaluate the y −intercept of the remaining choices:

    B. $y = \frac{3}{5}x + 3$: The y −intercept is 3. Because for $x = 0$, we have: $y = 3$.

C. $y = \frac{3}{5}x - 3$: In the same way, the y −intercept is −3.

Based on the graph, the y −intercept of the line g is −2. Therefore, the choice B is the correct answer.

18) Choice D is correct

We can find the answer by factoring the quadratic expression. First, we multiply the coefficient of the x^2 term by the constant term:

$-5 \times 2 = -10$.

Next, we need to find two numbers whose product is −10 and whose sum is −9, the coefficient of the x term. These numbers are −10 and 1.

So, we can rewrite the expression as: $-5x^2 - 10x + x + 2$.

Next, we group the terms: $(-5x^2 - 10x) + (x + 2)$.

Then we factor out the common factors from each group: $-5x(x + 2) + 1(x + 2)$.

Finally, we can write the expression as a product of two binomials: $(-5x + 1)(x + 2)$.

So, the answer is D.

19) Choice C is correct

According to the information in the table, when the value of x increases, then the value $k(x)$ first increases and then decreases. By checking the choices, we find that the parent functions A, B or D are strictly ascending. Only the parent function of choice C has this property.

20) Choice B is correct

Let x be the number of hours the painter spent painting the house. Then, the total cost can be expressed as $40x + 60 = 1,100$.

Subtracting 60 from both sides: $40x = 1,040$. Dividing by 40: $x = 26$.

Therefore, the painter spent 26 hours painting the house. The closest answer choice is B, 25 hours, but the correct answer is 26 hours.

21) Choice A is correct

The range of the function is the possible value for y. One of the choices A or C is the solution set. The image of the graph on the $y-$axis is equivalent to the range of the graph. Look at the following graph:

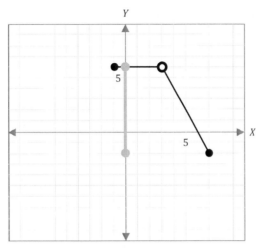

The interval $-2 \leq y \leq 6$ is the range of the function.

22) Choice D is correct

Yes, because the number of small backpacks is twice the number of large backpacks. 200 small backpacks and 100 large backpacks make a total of 300 backpacks, which is the combined total that the junior class needs. Additionally, since the number of small backpacks needed is twice the number of large backpacks needed, having twice as many small backpacks as large backpacks satisfies this condition. Therefore, it is reasonable for the junior class to order 100 large backpacks and 200 small backpacks.

23) Choice C is correct

$3x + x + x - 2 = x + x + x + 8$, combining like terms on each side of the given equation yields $5x - 2 = 3x + 8$. Adding 2 to both sides of $5x - 2 + 2 = 3x + 8 + 2 \rightarrow 5x = 3x + 10$. Subtracting $3x$ from both sides gives $5x - 3x = 3x + 10 - 3x \rightarrow 2x = 10$. Divide both sides of $2x = 10$ by 2 and yield $x = 5$.

Keystone Algebra I Practice Tests 6 Explanations

Section 2

24) The answer is 4

Given the coordinates of two points through which the line passes, first, find the slope of the line using the slope formula. $m = \frac{y_2 - y_1}{x_2 - x_1}$. Substituting in the known information $(x_1, y_1) = (2, 2), (x_2, y_2) = (0, 4), m = \frac{y_2 - y_1}{x_2 - x_1} = \frac{4-2}{0-(2)} = -1$.

Next, we can use the slope-intercept form of a linear equation, which is given by:

$y = mx + c$, where m is the slope and c is the y-intercept is 4, so we have:

$y = -x + 4$

To find the x-coordinate where the line crosses the x-axis, we can set y to 0:

$0 = -x + 4$

$x = 4$

Therefore, the value of m is 4.

25) The answer is 6

The four-term polynomial expression can be factored completely, by grouping, it as follows:

$(x^3 - 6x^2) + (3x - 18) = 0, x^2(x - 6) + 3(x - 6) = 0, (x - 6)(x^2 + 3) = 0.$

By zero product property, set each factor of the polynomial equal to 0 and solve each resulting equation for x. This gives $x = 6$ or $x = \pm i\sqrt{3}$, respectively. Because the question asks for the real value of x that satisfies the equation, the correct answer is 6.

26) The answer is 15

To solve the problem, plug the given information into the equation and solve for the variable f:

$$10 = \frac{(50 - 3f)}{0.5}$$

Multiplying both sides by 0.5: $5 = 50 - 3f$. Subtracting 50 from both sides: $-45 = -3f$.

Dividing both sides by -3: $f = 15$. So, the construction worker completes 15 wooden fences that week.

27) The answer is 14

Since the equations $x + 3y = 7$ and $2x + 6y = a$ represent the same line in the xy-plane, they must be equivalent equations. The expression $2x + 6y$ is two times the expression $x + 3y = 7$.

Thus, to be equivalent, a must be 2 times the number 7. Therefore, $a = 14$.

Keystone Algebra I Practice Tests 7 Explanations
Section 1

1) Choice C is correct

First, draw the function $k(x) = 2x^2 - 4$. For this purpose, consider the parent function of quadratic x^2.

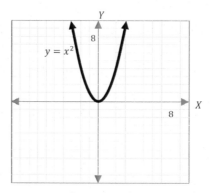

Next, get the graph of function $f(x) = 2x^2$ by compressing x^2 horizontally.

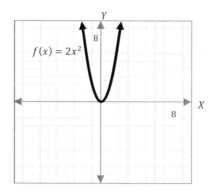

So, $k(x) = 2x^2 - 4$ is obtained by moving the graph $f(x)$ down by 4 units. The graph of $k(x)$ is as follows:

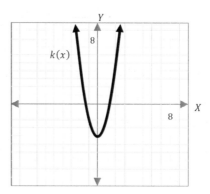

Then, choice C is correct.

2) Choice D is correct

The equation defining any line can be written in the form $y = mx + b$, where m is the slope of the line and b is the y-coordinate of the y-intercept. Line t passes through the point $(0, 4)$, which is the y-intercept. Therefore $b = 4$.

Calculating the slope using two points that line t passes through, $(-2, 0)$ and $(0, 4)$, gives $m = \frac{4-0}{0-(-2)} = \frac{4}{2} = 2$. Since $m = 2$ and $b = 4$, the equation of line t can be written as $y = 2x + 4$. Subtracting $2x$ to both sides yields $y - 2x = 4$.

3) Choice B is correct

The cost of purchasing x cookies is constant. Therefore, the cost of purchasing equation increases with the common difference from zero dollars. That is, the equation is linear and in the form of $y = dx$.

According to the graph information, the common difference is 3 units. So, the cost of purchasing equation is $y = 3x$.

Now, put the given order pairs at the choices in the equation. A point that does not apply to the equation is an additional point. Check the choices as:

 A. $(5, 15)$: $15 = 3 \times 5$
 B. $(7, 20)$: $20 \neq 3 \times 7$
 C. $(10, 30)$: $30 = 3 \times 10$
 D. $(6, 18)$: $18 = 3 \times 6$

Therefore, choice B is an additional point and the correct answer.

4) Choice B is correct

First, the new relationship is graphed on the same coordinate grid.

Now, let's check each of the statements:

A and D: You can see that the y-intercept of the two graphs does not change.

B. The rate of change of the new graph has increased. So, the new graph would be steeper than the original graph. In the same way, choice C is false.

Truck Loading

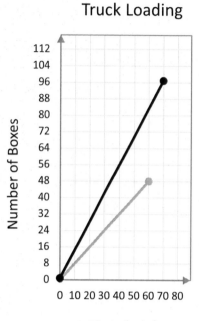

Time (min)

5) Choice C is correct

Since $4x = \frac{48}{3}$ and 48 divided by 3 is 16, which gives equation $4x = 16$, then dividing both sides of $4x = 16$ by 4 gives $x = 4$. Therefore $x - 2 = 4 - 2 = 2$ and 7 to the power of 2 is 49. Choices A, B, and D are incorrect.

6) Choice D is correct

For the present population to decrease by 20 percent, it must be multiplied by the factor of 0.8. Since the engineer estimates that the population will decrease by 20 percent every 10 years, the present population, 980,000, must be multiplied by $(0.8)^n$, where n is the number of 10-year periods that will have elapsed t years from now. After t years, the number of 10-year periods that have elapsed is $\frac{t}{10}$. Therefore, $980,000(0.8)^{\frac{t}{10}}$ represents the engineer's estimate of the population of the city t years from now.

7) Choice D is correct

Set a proportion: $\frac{1}{8} = \frac{3d+9}{x} \rightarrow x = 8(3d + 9) = 24d + 72$.

8) Choice B is correct

To find the answer to the problem, solve the equation for $r(x) = 0$: $\frac{4}{7}x + 12 = 0$.

Subtract 12 from both sides: $\frac{4}{7}x = -12$.

Multiply both sides by $\frac{7}{4}$: $x = -21$.

9) Choice C is correct

To answer this question, we need to understand the meaning of the function $f(x) = 6x + 120$. In this function, "x" represents the number of times the customer goes to the gym in one year. The constant term 120 represents the annual membership fee that the customer pays regardless of how many times he goes to the gym, and the term $6x$ represents the total cost the customer pays for "x" visits at a rate of $6 per visit.

Therefore, the correct answer is C. The variable "x" in the function $f(x) = 6x + 120$ represents the number of times the customer goes to the gym in one year.

10) Choice C is correct

To complete the purchase, the initial payment of $60 plus the w weekly payments of $30 must be equivalent to the $300 price of the television. The total, in dollars, of w weekly payment of $30 can be expressed by $30w$. It follows that $300 = 30w + 60$ can be used to find the number of weekly payments, w, required to complete the purchase.

11) Choice A is correct

For this question, a circular lawn with a radius of r feet has an area of $A(r) = \pi r^2$. The landscaper adds 10 square feet to the area, so the function that can be used to find the total area in square feet, $A(r)$, is $A(r) = \pi r^2 + 10$. Therefore, the correct answer is A.

12) Choice C is correct

If the regular price for a concert ticket is $100, and a different vendor offers a 10% discount on the regular price, then the discounted price would be:

Discounted price = Regular price − (Discount rate × Regular price)

Discounted price = $100 − (0.1 × $100) → Discounted price = $90

Therefore, each ticket costs $90 from the discounted vendor.

To calculate the savings, we need to find the difference between the total cost of purchasing 3 tickets at the regular price and the total cost of purchasing 3 tickets at the discounted price:

Regular price for 3 tickets = $100 \times 3 = 300

Discounted price for 3 tickets = $90 \times 3 = 270

Savings = Regular price for 3 tickets − Discounted price for 3 tickets

Savings = $300 − $270 = 30

So, the savings in dollars and cents by purchasing 3 tickets from the discounted vendor instead of the regular vendor would be $30.

13) Choice B is correct

The perimeter is the sum of the lengths of the sides of the polygon. The perimeter of the given polygon is $(2x) + (2x) + (x + 8) + (x − 5) + (3x − 2) + (x^2 + 2x)$. Simplify the expression as: $x^2 + 11x + 1$. The expression $x^2 + 11x + 1$ equals 181. Now, solve the equation below:

$x^2 + 11x + 1 = 181 \rightarrow x^2 + 11x − 180 = 0$.

Find the solution of the equation by using the formula: $x = \frac{-b \pm \sqrt{b^2 - 4ac}}{2a}$. The value of a, b, and c is 1, 11, and −180, respectively. So, we get:

$x = \frac{-(11) \pm \sqrt{(11)^2 - 4(1)(-180)}}{2(1)} = \frac{-11 \pm \sqrt{841}}{2} = \frac{-11 \pm 29}{2}$.

Therefore, $x = −20$, (which is a negative number, and is not acceptable for the length of the geometric sides) or $x = 9$.

14) Choice A is correct

To solve the system of equations:

$$2a = 9 − 5b$$
$$3b = a − 6$$

Rewrite the system of equations as:

$$2a + 5b = 9$$
$$a − 3b = 6$$

We can start by eliminating b by multiplying the first equation by 3 and the second equation by 5 to get:

$$3 \times (2a + 5b) = 3 \times (9)$$
$$5 \times (a - 3b) = 5 \times (6)$$
$$\rightarrow \quad 6a + 15b = 27$$
$$5a - 15b = 30$$

Next, we can add the two equations to eliminate b and solve for a:

$$11a = 57 \rightarrow a = \frac{57}{11}.$$

Therefore, the value of a in the solution to the system of equations is $\frac{57}{11}$, which means the answer is option A.

15) Choice A is correct

The range is the set of possible output values, which are shown on the $y-$axis. Get the image of the graph on the $y-$axis:

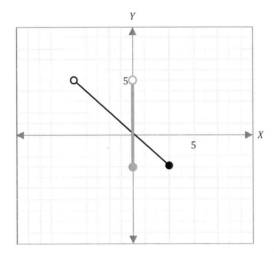

According to the above graph, the interval $-3 \leq y < 5$ is the range of the function f.

16) Choice B is correct

The vertex of a quadratic function in the form $f(x) = ax^2 + bx + c$ is given by the point $\left(-\frac{b}{2a}, f\left(-\frac{b}{2a} \right) \right)$.

In this case, the quadratic function is $g(x) = 2x^2 - 4x + 5$. We can find the $x-$coordinate of the vertex by using the formula $-\frac{b}{2a}$: $-\frac{b}{2a} = -\frac{-4}{2(2)} = 1$.

So, the $x-$coordinate of the vertex is 1. To find the $y-$coordinate of the vertex, we can plug in $x = 1$ into the equation for $g(x)$ and simplify: $g(1) = 2(1)^2 - 4(1) + 5 = 2 - 4 + 5 = 3$.

Therefore, the vertex of the graph of the quadratic function $g(x) = 2x^2 - 4x + 5$ is $(1,3)$, which corresponds to answer choice B.

17) Choice D is correct

Since $y = f(x)$, the value of $f(0)$ is equal to the value of $f(x)$, or y, when $x = 0$. The graph indicates that when $x = 0$, $y = 2$. It follows that value of $f(0) = 2$.

18) Choice D is correct

The value of x of the vertex in the equation of a quadratic in standard form is $x = \frac{-b}{2a}$.

(The standard equation of a quadratic is: $ax^2 + bx + c = 0$)

Let's find the vertex of each choice provided:

A. $y = 2x^2 + 5$ The vertex is: $(0, 5)$

B. $y = -2x^2 + 5$ The vertex is: $(0, 5)$

C. $y = x^2 + 2x + 5$ The vertex is: $(-1, 4)$

D. $= 4(x - 2)^2 + 5$

The vertex form of a parabola equation is in the form of $y = a(x - h)^2 + k$, where (h, k) is the vertex. Then $h = 2$ and $k = 5$. (This is the answer)

19) Choice C is correct

To solve the problem, we can use the given information to write an inequality that relates the number of small coffees sold to the total revenue from coffee sales.

Let s be the number of small coffees sold. The total revenue from coffee sales is given by: Revenue $= (2.75 \times s) + (3.50 \times 90) + (4.25 \times 60)$.

Simplifying the expression, we get Revenue $= 2.75s + 315 + 255 \rightarrow$ Revenue $= 2.75s + 570$.

Since the revenue is between \$900 and \$1000, we can write the inequality:

$900 \le 2.75s + 570 \le 1000$.

Subtracting 570 from all parts of the inequality, we get $330 \le 2.75s \le 430$.

Dividing all parts of the inequality by 2.75, we get $120 \le s \le 156.36$.

Since s is a whole number, the possible values of s are between 120 and 156, inclusive. Therefore, the correct answer is C. $110 \le s \le 140$ (rounded to the nearest multiple of 10).

20) Choice A is correct

When two variables are inversely proportional, their product is constant. In other words, as one variable increases, the other variable decreases in such a way that the product of the two remains the same.

We can use this concept to set up an equation for the problem:

$z = \dfrac{k}{w} \rightarrow z \times w = k$, where k is a constant.

We can solve for k by plugging in the given values:

$30 \times 6 = k \rightarrow k = 180$.

Now we can use this value to write the inverse variation equation: $z \times w = 180$.

Dividing both sides by w: $z = \dfrac{180}{w}$.

Therefore, the correct function is $z = \dfrac{180}{w}$.

21) Choice D is correct

First, we remove the outliers (if any). Point $(60,2)$ is an outlier. Then, we draw an approximation of the trend line. Next, we find the point of intersection on the trend line with $x = 40$.

See the trend line and the point of intersection with line $x = 40$ in the scatterplot below:

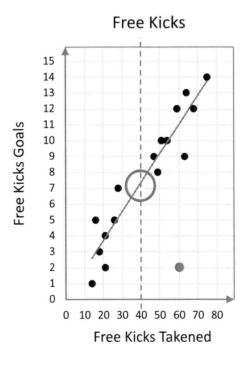

Free Kicks

Choice D is correct.

22) Choice D is correct

For the equation of the line in form $y = mx + b$, the slope is m. Also, the y−intercept is point $(0, b)$, which we get b by solving the equation $y = mx + b$ for $x = 0$.

To find the suitable graph, determine the slope and y−intercept of the line $y = \frac{2}{3}x - \frac{8}{6}$: $m = \frac{2}{3}$ and y−intercept $= -\frac{8}{6}$. By dividing the slope and y−intercept by $-\frac{1}{3}$, the new graph is

$$y = -2x + 4.$$

Find a graph that shows a line with slope -2 that passes through the point $(0,4)$. (Choice D).

23) Choice B is correct

To solve the check each representation of the choices:

A. It's enough, one of the ordered pairs does not satisfy the equation. For the value $x = -3$, then $h(-3) = -\frac{1}{2}(3(-3) + 11) = -1 \neq 4$, which is not the same as the value in the map.

B. After, checking that all the points in the table apply in the equation. You can see that option B is the correct answer.

C. In the same way at choice A, for $x = -4$, we get $h(-4) = -\frac{1}{2}(3(-4) + 11) = \frac{1}{2}$. Which is not equal to 1. Then, it's incorrect.

D. The slope of the graph is positive, while the slope of the given equation is negative.

Keystone Algebra I Practice Tests 7 Explanations
Section 2

24) The answer is 4

The sum of the given expressions is $(-4x^2 + 3x - 24) + (7x^2 - 8x + 18)$. Combining like terms yields $3x^2 - 5x - 6$. Based on the form of the given equation, $a = 3$, $b = -5$, and $c = -6$. Therefore, $a + b - c = 3 + (-5) - (-6) = 4$.

25) The answer is 4

$t^2 - 16 = 0 \rightarrow (t - 4)(t + 4) = 0$. So $(t - 4) = 0$ or $(t + 4) = 0$

$(t - 4) = 0 \rightarrow t = 4$

$(t + 4) = 0 \rightarrow t = -4$

t has two values: $4, -4$. Because the question is written $t > 0$ so $t = 4$.

26) The answer is 3

Let y be the number of international tourist arrivals in Russia in 2012, and let x be the number of these arrivals in 2011. It's given that y is 13.5% greater than x, or $y = 1.135x$. The table gives that $y = 24.7$, so $24.7 = 1.135x$. Dividing both sides of this equation by 1.135 yields $\frac{24.7}{1.135} = x$, or $x \approx 21.8$ million arrivals. The difference in the number of tourist arrivals between these two years is 24.7 million -21.8 million $= 2.9$ million. Therefore, the value of k is 3 when rounded to the nearest integer.

27) The answer is $39,366$

The formula of population growth is in the form of an exponential function as $p(w) = p_0(r)^w$, where p_0 is the initial population and r is the common ratio between the terms. Find the common ratio by dividing each term by the previous term. So, we get:

$\frac{6}{2} = 3$, $\frac{18}{6} = 3$, and $\frac{54}{18} = 3$.

Then, the common ratio is 3. Substitute the common ratio in the equation $p(w) = p_0(r)^w$. We have:

$$p(w) = p_0(3)^w$$

Next, plug one of the ordered pair from the table to evaluate the value of p_0. We consider point $(1,6)$: $6 = p_0(3)^1 \rightarrow 3p_0 = 6 \rightarrow p_0 = 2$.

Now, substitute $w = 9$ in the equation $p(w) = 2(3)^w$, and obtain the value of $p(9)$:

$p(9) = 2(3)^9 = 2 \times 19,683 = 39,366$

Keystone Algebra I Practice Tests 8 Explanations
Section 1

1) Choice D is correct

To solve the equation $4x^2 - 9 = 12x$, we can start by bringing all the terms to one side of the equation, so that we have: $4x^2 - 12x - 9 = 0$.

Next, we can use the quadratic formula to find the values of x that satisfy this equation. The quadratic formula is:

$$x_{1,2} = \frac{-b \pm \sqrt{b^2 - 4ac}}{2a}$$

For our equation, we have $a = 4$, $b = -12$, and $c = -9$. Substituting these values into the quadratic formula, we get:

$$x_{1,2} = \frac{-(-12) \pm \sqrt{(-12)^2 - 4(4)(-9)}}{2(4)} \rightarrow x_{1,2} = \frac{12 \pm \sqrt{144 + 144}}{8}$$

$$\rightarrow x_{1,2} = \frac{12 \pm 12\sqrt{2}}{8} = \frac{3 \pm 3\sqrt{2}}{2}$$

Therefore, the solutions to the equation $4x^2 - 9 = 12x$ are $x_1 = \frac{3+3\sqrt{2}}{2}$ and $x_2 = \frac{3-3\sqrt{2}}{2}$.

So, the rational part of the solution is $\frac{3}{2}$ and $-\frac{3}{2}$.

2) Choice D is correct

First, distribute the 2 and 5: $5x - 15 - 2x - 10 = -13$. Combine like terms: $3x - 25 = -13$. Add 25 to both sides: $3x = 12$. Divide both sides by 3: $x = 4$. The solution is $x = 4$, which corresponds to option D.

3) Choice B is correct

To find the inequality that represents the graph of the problem, we first get the equation of the line passing through points $(2b, 0)$ and $(0, b)$ based on the graph, such that the number b is negative. The slope of the line passing through (x_1, y_1) and (x_2, y_2): $m = \frac{y_2 - y_1}{x_2 - x_1}$. So, for the points $(2b, 0)$ and $(0, b)$, we get:

$$m = \frac{b - 0}{0 - 2b} = -\frac{b}{2b} = -\frac{1}{2}.$$

Then, write the equation of the line passes through the point $(0, b)$ with the slope $m = -\frac{1}{2}$:

$$y - b = -\frac{1}{2}(x - 0) \rightarrow y = -\frac{1}{2}x + b.$$

We can rewrite the equation as below: $x + 2y = 2b$. Next, put some points like (b, b) of the shaded area in the equation of the function to get the direction of the inequality.

(b, b): $b + 2(b) = 3b$, we know that b is negative, then $3b < 2b$. Answer set, therefore the equation of the inequality is $x + 2y \leq 2b$.

4) Choice A is correct

To expand the expression $(2n - 5)(3n + 4)$, we can use the distributive property of multiplication:

$$(2n - 5)(3n + 4) = 2n \times 3n + 2n \times 4 - 5 \times 3n - 5 \times 4.$$

Simplifying, we get:

$$2n \times 3n + 2n \times 4 - 5 \times 3n - 5 \times 4 = 6n^2 + 8n - 15n - 20.$$

Combining like terms, we get:

$$6n^2 + 8n - 15n - 20 = 6n^2 - 7n - 20.$$

Therefore, the expression that is equivalent to $(2n - 5)(3n + 4)$ is $6n^2 - 7n - 20$.

5) Choice C is correct

The given function is $g(x) = x^2 - 49$, which can be factored as $0 = (x + 7)(x - 7)$. Therefore, the zeros of the function are $x = -7$ and $x = 7$.

Option C is correct because it shows the correct factorization of the function and the corresponding zeros. Options A and B both show a repeated factorization which is incorrect. Option D shows a different factorization with zeros that don't match the zeros of the function.

6) Choice D is correct

The range of a function is the set of output values, which is $f(x)$ here. Therefore, we have:

$$\{-7, -3, 4, 9\}$$

Note that no input value of the function gives an output of 1.

7) Choice B is correct

We check the graphs to find a choice that intersects the vertical lines parallel to the y −axis of the graph at least at one point of the domain of the graph in more than one point.

Graph B is not a function because there are two output values for the graph at the specified location.

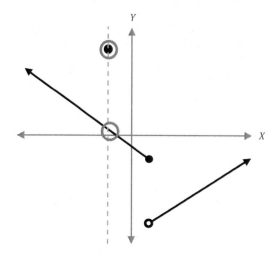

8) Choice A is correct

To solve the equation $2x^2 + 5x - 3 = 0$, we can use the quadratic formula, which states that if $ax^2 + bx + c = 0$, then:

$x_{1,2} = \frac{-b \pm \sqrt{b^2 - 4ac}}{2a}$

Plugging in $a = 2$, $b = 5$, and $c = -3$, we get:

$x_{1,2} = \frac{-5 \pm \sqrt{5^2 - 4(2)(-3)}}{2(2)} \rightarrow x_{1,2} = \frac{-5 \pm \sqrt{49}}{4} \rightarrow x_{1,2} = \frac{-5 \pm 7}{4}.$

So, the solutions to the equation are $x_1 = -3$ and $x_2 = \frac{1}{2}$. Since we're looking for a positive solution, the answer is $x = \frac{1}{2}$.

9) Choice D is correct

According to the four quadrants of the coordinate plane:

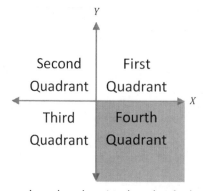

The two lines must converge toward each other in the shaded area. Check the choices:

A. The point of intersection of the two lines is in the third quadrant.

B. The two lines are parallel and the system of equations has no solution.

C. Two lines intersect in the first quadrant.

D. In choice D, the two lines converge in the fourth quadrant and the two lines intersect each other. Therefore, this graph has one solution in the fourth quadrant.

10) Choice B is correct

The function $y = 5x - 3x^2 + 2$ is quadratic. So, the domain y is all real numbers. According to the information in the table, the input values are the set $\{-2, -1, 0, 2, 3\}$. We evaluate the y −values of the given function as:

$x = -2: y = 5(-2) - 3(-2)^2 + 2 = -20$

$x = -1: y = 5(-1) - 3(-1)^2 + 2 = -6$

$x = 0: y = 5(0) - 3(0)^2 + 2 = 2$

$x = 2: y = 5(2) - 3(2)^2 + 2 = 0$

$x = 3: y = 5(3) - 3(3)^2 + 2 = -10$

Compare the obtained values to the tables. Therefore, the choice B is the correct answer.

11) Choice C is correct

To find the values of x when $x^2 + 2x - 8 = -5$ through the given graph, it is enough to intercept the graph with line $y = -5$. The obtained points are equivalent to the requested values. Look at the graph below:

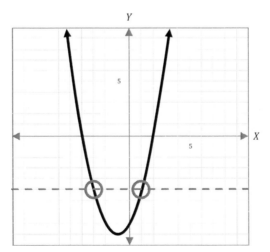

We see that line $y = -5$ intersects the graph at points $x = 1$ and $x = -3$. Therefore, choice C is correct.

12) Choice C is correct

The slope of both graphs is positive. So, to make graph g, the slope of graph f must be multiplied by a positive number. In addition, the slope of the graph g is steeper than the original graph. Therefore, the slope of the graph g is multiplied by a number greater than one. On the other hand, we can see that graph g is 4 units higher than the graph f. The only choice that meets these conditions is option C.

13) Choice C is correct

Based on the information in the table, the function g is decreasing. So, choices 1 and 2 are false. Next, by dividing each value of g by its previous value, we get:

$\frac{9,750}{10,000} = 0.975, \frac{9,506}{9,750} \cong 0.975, \cdots,$ and $\frac{9,037}{9,269} \cong 0.975.$

We can see that the values of the function are changing with a ratio of 0.975 or 97.5%. In other words, the values of the function are decreasing with a ratio of $97.5\% = (100 - 2.5)\%$. The reduction percentage is 2.5 or $2\frac{1}{2}$.

14) Choice A is correct

If $f(x) = 3x + 4(x + 1) + 2$, then find $f(4x)$ by substituting $4x$ for every x in the function. This gives: $f(4x) = 3(4x) + 4(4x + 1) + 2,$

It simplifies to: $f(4x) = 3(4x) + 4(4x + 1) + 2 = 12x + 16x + 4 + 2 = 28x + 6.$

15) Choice B is correct

To solve the system of equations:

$$3x + y = 15$$
$$-2x + 4y = 10$$

We can use the method of elimination. We want to eliminate one of the variables, so we can start by eliminating x by multiplying the second equation by $\frac{3}{2}$ to get:

$$3x + y = 15$$
$$\frac{3}{2} \times (-2x + 4y) = \frac{3}{2} \times (10) \rightarrow \begin{array}{l} 3x + y = 15 \\ -3x + 6y = 15 \end{array}$$

Next, we can add the two equations to eliminate y and solve for x:

$3x + y + (-3x + 6y) = 15 + 15 \rightarrow 7y = 30 \rightarrow y = \frac{30}{7}.$

Now, substitute $y = \frac{30}{7}$, in the first equation and solve:

$$3x + \left(\frac{30}{7}\right) = 15 \rightarrow 3x = 15 - \frac{30}{7} \rightarrow 3x = \frac{105-30}{7} = \frac{75}{7}$$

$$\rightarrow x = \frac{25}{7} =$$

Therefore, the solution of a system of equations is $\left(\frac{25}{7}, \frac{30}{7}\right)$, which means the answer is option B.

16) Choice D is correct

The smallest y-coordinate belongs to the point with coordinates $(3, -4)$.

The minimum value of the graph is $f(3) = -4$. Therefore, the value of $f(x)$ is at its minimum when x equals to 3.

17) Choice C is correct

Expanding the left side of the equation and simplifying, we get:

$1 + 3m - 12 = 7m \rightarrow 3m - 11 = 7m$.

Subtracting $3m$, we get: $-11 = 4m$. Dividing both sides by 4, we get $x = -\frac{11}{4}$.

Therefore, the solution to the equation is choice C, $x = -\frac{11}{4} = -2.75$.

18) Choice D is correct

For this purpose, it is necessary that each ordered pair of the content question is available in the corresponding relationship. Now, Check them out:

A. For the ordered pair $(0,3)$, if $x = 0$, then $g(0) = (0)^2 + 2(0) - 3 = -3$. Therefore, It's Not true!

B. In choice B, the ordered pair is as follows: $(-3, -5)$, $(-1, -4)$, $(0,0)$, and $(2,4)$. which is different from the content of the question.

C. Choice C is similar to choice B.

D. Choice D represents the same relationship as g. All the points of the function g are marked in graph D below:

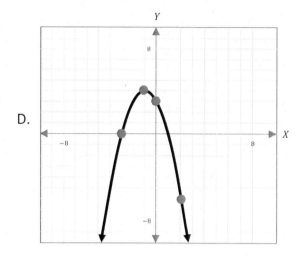

D.

19) Choice A is correct

There are 14 students in class 2 that are given only apples and there are 23 students in class 2. Therefore, the fraction of students in class 2 given only apples is $\frac{14}{23}$.

20) Choice D is correct

Since $h(x) = 1 - g(x)$, substituting 0 for x yields $h(0) = 1 - g(0)$.

Evaluating $g(0) = 2(0) - 1 = -1$. Therefore, $h(0) = 1 - (-1) = 2$.

21) Choice A is correct

In the graph, the x −intercept equals the time required to move the elevator from the highest floor to the ground floor. It's 25 seconds.

The elevator motion graph is linear. So, the rate of motion is constant. Therefore, the model equation of this graph is $y = -mx + b$, where m is the rate at which the moved elevator and b is the y −intercept of the line.

Since the height of the tower does not change. So, the y −intercept is 100. If the rate at which the moved elevator is changed to 6.25 meters per second, then $m = 6.25$. So, the model of elevator motion is as

$$y = -6.25x + 100$$

Next, evaluate the x −intercept of this model and compare it to the initial value of the x −intercept.

$$y = 0 \rightarrow -6.25x + 100 = 0 \rightarrow -6.25x = -100 \rightarrow x = 16$$

The difference between the two values is 2 units. The required time has been reduced by 9 seconds.

22) Choice A is correct

To solve this problem, find two numbers whose product is -30 and whose sum is 13, the coefficient of the x term. It seems that the numbers are 15 and -2. Rewrite the expression as $x^2 + 15x - 2x - 30$. Group the terms: $(x^2 + 15x) + (-2x - 30)$. Then, factor out the common factors from each group: $x(x + 15) - 2(x + 15) = (x - 2)(x + 15)$.

23) Choice C is correct

Since the number of mistakes has decreased with the increase in the average number of study hours, it shows that the variables are related, but they move in opposite directions from one another. As one increases, the other will decrease. That means the correction is negative. Therefore, the choice C is correct.

Keystone Algebra I Practice Tests 8 Explanations
Section 2

24) The answer is 8

$x^2 + 6x + r = (x + 2)(x + p) = x^2 + (2 + p)x + 2p$, on the left side of the equation the coefficient of x is 6, and on the right side of the equation, the coefficient of x is $2 + p$. Thus $2 + p = 6 \rightarrow p = 4$ and $r = 2p = 2(4) = 8$.

25) The answer is 6

We must first calculate the slope of the function f. Given that function f passes through points $(-2, 1)$ and $(0, 4)$, its slope is equal to: $\frac{4-1}{0-(-2)} = \frac{3}{2}$.

The slope of the line perpendicular to this line is $m_1 \times m_2 = -1 \Rightarrow \frac{3}{2} \times m_2 = -1 \Rightarrow m_2 = -\frac{2}{3}$.

The equation that defines function g passes through the point $(0, 4)$ is:

$g(x) = -\frac{2}{3}x + b \rightarrow 4 = -\frac{2}{3}(0) + b \rightarrow 4 = 0 + b \rightarrow b = 4$.

So, the equation of g is $g(x) = -\frac{2}{3}x + 4$.

The point of collision of function g with the x-axis is obtained by placing 0 instead of y in the function. Then: $0 = -\frac{2}{3}x + 4 \rightarrow \frac{2}{3}x = 4 \rightarrow x = 6$.

26) The answer is 12

The number of employees, E, expected to be employed by the store y years after the store opened can be modeled by the equation $E = cy + d$, where c represents the constant rate of change in the number of employees each year and d represents the number of employees with which the store opened. The store's growth plan assumes that 5 employees will be hired each year, so $c = 5$. The number of employees the company opened with was 12, so $d = 12$.

27) The answer is $\frac{1}{2}$

The intersection points of the graphs of $y = 4x^2 - 3x$ and $y = -x$ can be found by solving the system consisting of these two equations. To solve the system, substitute $-x$ for y in the first equation. This gives $-x = 4x^2 - 3x$. Adding x to both sides of the equation gives $0 = 4x^2 - 2x$. Factoring $2x$ out of each term on the right-hand side of the equation gives $2x(2x - 1) = 0$. Therefore, the possible values for x are 0 and $\frac{1}{2}$. Since $y = -x$, the two intersection points are $(0, 0)$ and $\left(\frac{1}{2}, -\frac{1}{2}\right)$. Therefore, $c = \frac{1}{2}$.

Keystone Algebra I Practice Tests 9 Explanations
Section 1

1) Choice A is correct

If $x - a$ is a factor of $g(x)$, then $g(a)$ must equal 0. Based on the table $g(-1) = 0$ and $g(5) = 0$. Therefore, $x + 1$ and $x - 5$ are factors of $g(x)$.

2) Choice B is correct

A column of 29 stacked wooden sheets is about $60\frac{3}{5}$ centimeters tall, which is slightly less than 61 centimeters tall. Therefore, a column of stacked wooden sheets that is 61 centimeters tall would contain slightly more than 29 wooden sheets. It can then be reasoned that because 122 meters are twice 61 meters, a column of stacked wooden sheets that is 122 meters tall would contain slightly more than twice as many wooden sheets; that is, slightly more than 58 wooden sheets. An alternate approach is to write proportion that compares the column height to the number of wooden sheets, or $\dfrac{60\frac{3}{5}\ meters}{29\ wooden\ sheets} = \dfrac{122\ meters}{x\ wooden\ sheets}$, where x is the number of coins in a 122-centimeter-tall column. Multiplying each side of the proportion gives $60\frac{3}{5}x = 3{,}538 \rightarrow \frac{303}{5}x = 3{,}538$. Solving for x gives $x = \frac{3{,}538 \times 5}{303}$, which is approximately 58. Therefore, of the given choices, 59 is closest to the number of wooden sheets it would take to build a 122-centimeter-tall column.

3) Choice A is correct

To solve this problem, we substitute $z = -5$ into the inequality and simplify it as follows:

$z = -5 \rightarrow 2w + 4(-5) \le 28 \rightarrow 2w - 20 \le 28$

$$\rightarrow 2w \le 48$$

$$\rightarrow w \le 24$$

Therefore, the set of possible values for the variable "w" that satisfies the inequality is $w \le 24$. So, the correct inequality statement is A.

4) Choice B is correct

Rearrange the ordered pair from the smallest value of the first component to the biggest value.

$$\{(-2,7), (-1,2), (0,-1), (3,2), (5,14)\}$$

Since the range of the function is first decreasing and then increasing with the increase of x, we conclude that between the choices, only the parent function of quadratic has this property.

5) Choice B is correct

Since the basketball player scored at least 15 points more than the previous record, we can write $p \geq r + 15$.

This inequality ensures that p is at least 15 more than r, and thus all possible values of p in terms of r are given by this inequality. Therefore, the answer is B.

6) Choice B is correct

The total length of the suspension bridge, including the towers, can be found by adding the length of the n bridge sections to the height of the two towers. Each section is $48.2m$ long and there are n sections, so the length of the bridge sections is $48.2n$. The height of the two towers is $125.6m$ each, so their total height is $2 \times 125.6 = 251.2m$. Therefore, the function that can be used to find the total length of the bridge in meters, including the towers, is:

$$L(x) = 48.2n + 251.2$$

So, the correct answer is B.

7) Choice A is correct

There can be 0, 1, or 2 solutions to a quadratic equation. In standard form, a quadratic equation is written as $ax^2 + bx + c = 0$.

For the quadratic equation, the expression $b^2 - 4ac$ is called the discriminant. If the discriminant is positive, there are 2 distinct solutions for the quadratic equation. If the discriminant is 0, there is one solution for the quadratic equation and if it is negative the equation does not have any solutions.

To find the number of solutions for $2x^2 + 3 = 3x$, first, rewrite it as $2x^2 - 3x + 3 = 0$.

Find the value of the discriminant. $b^2 - 4ac = (-3)^2 - 4(2)(3) = 9 - 24 = -15$

Since the discriminant is negative, the quadratic equation has no distinct solutions.

8) Choice D is correct

To find the x −intercepts of the graph of the quadratic function, we need to set $g(x) = 0$ and solve for x. For the function $g(x) = -3x^2 + 9x - 6$, we have: $-3x^2 + 9x - 6 = 0$. Dividing both sides by -3, we get $x^2 - 3x + 2 = 0$.

To solve this quadratic equation, we can use the quadratic formula:

$$x_{1,2} = \frac{-b \pm \sqrt{b^2 - 4ac}}{2a}$$

where $a = 1$, $b = -3$, and $c = 2$.

Plugging in these values, we get:

$$x_{1,2} = \frac{-(-3) \pm \sqrt{(-3)^2 - 4(1)(2)}}{2(1)} = \frac{3 \pm \sqrt{9 - 8}}{2} = \frac{3 \pm 1}{2}$$

So, the $x-$intercepts of the graph of the function $g(x)$ are $x = 2$ and $x = 1$.

9) Choice D is correct

Since 8 can be rewritten as 2^3, $8^{\frac{2}{5}}$ is equivalent to $2^{3\left(\frac{2}{5}\right)}$. Applying the properties of exponents gives $2^{3 \times \frac{2}{5}} = 2^{\frac{6}{5}}$. This can be written as $2^{\frac{5}{5}} \cdot 2^{\frac{1}{5}}$, $2^{\frac{5}{5}}$ is equal to 2, and $2^{\frac{1}{5}}$ is equal to $\sqrt[5]{2}$ (remember $b^{\frac{m}{n}} = \sqrt[n]{b^m}$). So, $8^{\frac{2}{5}}$ is equal to $2\sqrt[5]{2}$.

10) Choice C is correct

Since the graph crosses the y-axis at $(0, r)$, then substituting 0 for x and r for y in $r = -3(0)^2 + 12(0) + 6$ creates a true statement: $r = -3(0)^2 + 12(0) + 6$, or $r = 6$.

Choice C represents the chart.

11) Choice C is correct

Let a equal the number of 120-pound packages, and let b equal the number of 100-pound packages. It's given that the total weight of the packages can be at most 1,100 pounds: the inequality $120a + 100b \leq 1,100$ represents this situation. It's also given that the helicopter must carry at least 10 packages: the inequality $a + b \geq 10$ represents this situation. Values of a and b that satisfy these two inequalities represent the allowable numbers of 120-pound packages and 100-pound packages the helicopter can transport. To maximize the number of 120-pound packages, a, in the helicopter, the number of 100-pound packages, b, in the helicopter needs to be minimized. Expressing b in terms of a in the second inequality yields $b \geq 10 - a$, so the minimum value of b is equal to $10 - a$. Substituting $10 - a$ for b in the first inequality results in

$120a + 100(10 - a) \leq 1,100$. Using the distributive property to rewrite this inequality yields $120a + 1,000 - 100a \leq 1,100$ or $20a + 1,000 \leq 1,100$. Subtracting 1,000 from both sides of this inequality yields $20a \leq 100$. Dividing both sides of this inequality by 20 results in $a \leq 5$. This means that the maximum number of 120-pound packages that the helicopter can carry per trip is 5.

12) Choice A is correct

The equation of a line with slope m and passing through the point (x_1, y_1) can be written as $y - y_1 = m(x - x_1)$. In this case, we are given that the slope is 2 and the point $(3,5)$ is on the line. So, we have $y - 5 = 2(x - 3)$. Expanding the right-hand side gives $y - 5 = 2x - 6$. Adding 5 to both sides gives $y = 2x - 1$.

Therefore, the equation of the line is A.

13) Choice D is correct

The solution of the equation $y = 3$ is equivalent to the intersection of the graph $y = mx + b$ and the horizontal line $y = 3$. Look at the graph below.

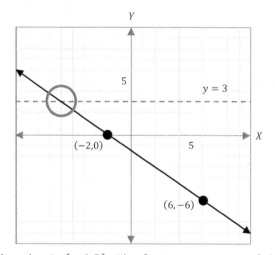

The intersection is the ordered pair $(-6,3)$. The first component of this ordered pair is -6 and is equivalent to the solution of the problem. Choice D is the correct answer.

In another way, you can get the correct answer by writing the equation of the graph $y = mx + b$. Next, solve the equation $mx + b = 3$.

14) Choice A is correct

According to the table, the value of y increases by $\frac{21}{10} - \frac{8}{5} = \frac{21-16}{10} = \frac{5}{10} = \frac{1}{2}$ every time the value of x increases by 1. It follows that the simplest equation relating y to x is linear and of the form $y = \frac{1}{2}x + b$ for some constant b. Furthermore, the ordered pair $\left(2, \frac{8}{5}\right)$ from the table must satisfy this equation. Substituting 2 for x and $\frac{8}{5}$ for y in the equation $y = \frac{1}{2}x + b$ gives $\frac{8}{5} = \frac{1}{2}(2) + b$. Solving this equation for b gives $b = \frac{3}{5}$. Therefore, the equation in choice A correctly relates y to x.

15) Choice D is correct

To compare the graphs of $f(x) = -2x + 5$ and $g(x) = -\frac{1}{2}x + 3$, we can look at their slopes and y−intercepts.

The slope of $f(x)$ is -2, which means that for every 1 unit increase in x, the value of $f(x)$ decreases by 2 units.

The slope of $g(x)$ is $-\frac{1}{2}$, which means that for every 1 unit increase in x, the value of $g(x)$ decreases by $\frac{1}{2}$ unit.

Since the slope of $f(x)$ is greater in magnitude than the slope of $g(x)$, the graph of $f(x)$ is steeper than the graph of $g(x)$. Therefore, the answer is D. The graph of f is steeper than the graph of g.

The y−intercept of $f(x)$ is 5, which means that $f(x)$ intersects the y−axis at $(0,5)$.

The y−intercept of $g(x)$ is 3, which means that $g(x)$ intersects the y−axis at $(0,3)$.

Since the y−intercepts of $f(x)$ and $g(x)$ are different, the answer is not B. The graph of f does not have the same y−intercept as the graph of g.

Finally, since the slopes of $f(x)$ and $g(x)$ are different, the answer is not C. The graph of f is not parallel to the graph of g.

16) Choice B is correct

To find the greatest value in the range for renting a bicycle from the rental shop, we need to consider the different scenarios that can occur based on the number of hours rented:

- If the bicycle is rented for 5 or fewer hours, the cost will be $10 per hour.
- If the bicycle is rented for more than 5 hours, the cost will be $65 ($50 for the first 5 hours and $15 for the late fee).

Therefore, the greatest value in the range for this situation is $65, which is the maximum cost that can be charged regardless of how many hours the bicycle is rented beyond the first 5 hours.

17) Choice A is correct

To find the average annual electricity consumption of the town, we need to multiply the average monthly consumption by 12:

$$500\,\frac{kWh}{month} \times 12\,\frac{month}{year} = 6,000\,\frac{kWh}{year}$$

For the first six months, the town consumed $2,800\,kWh$. So, the town needs to consume:

$$6,000\,kWh - 2,800\,kWh = 3,200\,kWh$$

For the rest of the year.

If the town is expected to consume between 400 and 550kWh per month for the rest of the year, it will take at least 6 months to consume 3,200kWh. Therefore, the answer is A.

18) Choice A is correct

The original function for the airplane's altitude during descent is $f(x) = -200x + 20,000$. This means that for every horizontal mile the airplane travels, it descends 200 feet. The constant term, 20,000, represents the altitude the airplane starts its descent. After new regulations are put in place, the function for the airplane's altitude during descent becomes $g(x) = -200x + 21,000$. This means that the airplane still descends 200 feet for every horizontal mile, but now it starts its descent from an altitude of 21,000 feet, which is 1,000 feet higher than before. Therefore, the correct statement is "The airplane starts its descent from an altitude 1,000 feet higher".

19) Choice B is correct

Subtracting 29 from both sides of the equation $a = 2.35b + 29$ gives $a - 29 = 2.35b$. Then dividing both sides of $a - 29 = 2.35b$ by 2.35 gives $b = \frac{a-29}{2.35}$.

20) Choice C is correct

From the problem, we know that:

Total tickets sold = 300, and Total revenue: $2250 \leq r \leq \$2500$.

Let a be the number of adult tickets sold. Then, the number of child tickets sold can be expressed in terms of a as follows: Children = $300 - a$. Then:

Revenue from adult tickets = $9a$, and Revenue from child tickets = $6.5(300 - a)$.

Using the given revenue range: $2250 \leq 9a + 6.5(300 - a) \leq \$2500$. Simplifying this inequality: $300 \leq 2.5a \leq 550$. Since a cannot be negative, we know that $a < 300$, therefore, the possible range for a is $120 \leq a \leq 220$, which corresponds to answer choice C.

21) Choice B is correct

Look at the information in the table to see how the values of $f(x)$ change with increasing values of x. We see the function f is increasing because when $x_1 < x_2$, then $f(x_1) < f(x_2)$. Therefore, C or D cannot be about the information in this table!

In the next step, evaluate the rate of change of the function values. Use the formula of the rate of change for function f as:

Rate of Change $= \frac{f(b)-f(a)}{b-a}$,

Where a and b is two number in the domain of f and $a < b$.

By evaluating the rate of change, we understand that the rate of change is constant and equal to 32 units. Hence, the equation related to the table is linear with a positive slope of 32. Therefore, choice B is the correct answer.

22) Choice A is correct

Since the cost of shipping a package varies directly with its weight, we can use the formula $y = kx$, where y is the cost, x is the weight, and k is the constant of proportionality.

We are given that the cost of shipping a 4-pound package is $10.80, so we can set up an equation using this information: $10.80 = k(4)$. Solving for k, we get $k = 2.7$.

Now, we can use this value of k to find the cost of shipping a 2.5-pound package:

$y = 2.7(2.5) = 6.75$.

Therefore, the cost of shipping a 2.5-pound package is $6.75, which is answer A.

23) Choice B is correct

To solve this problem, let e represent the number of evening dresses, and c represent the number of cocktail dresses. We can set up a system of two equations based on the given information:

$e + c = 200$ (The total number of dresses)

$\frac{e}{c} = \frac{3}{5} \rightarrow e = \frac{3}{5}c$ (There are $\frac{3}{5}$ times as many evening dresses as cocktail dresses)

Substitute the second equation into the first equation to get: $\frac{3}{5}c + c = 200$. Simplify and solve for c: $\frac{8}{5}c = 200 \rightarrow c = 125$. Use the second equation to find e: $e = \frac{3}{5} \times 125 = 75$.

Therefore, there are 75 evening dresses and 125 cocktail dresses on display. The answer is B.

Keystone Algebra I Practice Tests 9 Explanations
Section 2

24) The answer is 2

The line k is parallel to the line $y = \frac{3}{4}x + 3$ so they have the same slopes. The slope of the line $y = \frac{3}{4}x + 3$ line is $\frac{3}{4}$. Therefore, the slope of the line k is also equal to $\frac{3}{4}$.

So, the equation of line k in the slope-intercept form is $y = \frac{3}{4}x - 7$.

By placing the point m on the line k, the value of b will be equal to:

$b = \frac{3}{4}(12) - 7 \rightarrow b = 9 - 7 \rightarrow b = 2$.

25) The answer is 80

Let x be the number of kilometers that is equal to 50 miles. Since 10 miles is equal to 16 kilometers, it follows that $\frac{50}{10} = \frac{x}{16}$. Solving this proportion for x yields $10x = 800$ or $x = 80$.

26) The answer is 3

Solve $x + y = 7$ for x: add $-y$ to both sides $x + y + (-y) = 7 + (-y) \rightarrow x = -y + 7$.

Step 1: Substitute $(-y + 7)$ for x in $x + 2y = 11$:

$x + 2y = 11$

$-y + 7 + 2y = 11$

Simplify both sides of the equation $y + 7 = 11$ and add -7 to both sides

$y + 7 + (-7) = 11 + (-7) \rightarrow y = 4$.

Step 2: Substitute 4 for y in $x = -y + 7$:

$x = -y + 7 \rightarrow x = -4 + 7 \rightarrow x = 3$.

27) The answer is 8

It's given that the deductions reduce the original amount of taxes owed by \$1,536.00. Since the deductions reduce the original tax amount owed by $x\%$, the equation $\frac{1,536.00}{19,200} = \frac{x}{100}$ can be used to find this percent decrease, x. Multiplying both sides of this equation by 100 yields $\frac{153,600}{19,200} = x$, or $8 = x$. Thus, the tax deductions reduce the original tax amount owed by approximately 8%.

Keystone Algebra I Practice Tests 10 Explanations
Section 1

1) Choice B is correct

The graph intersects the x −axis at two points. So, the function f has two real roots (One of choices B or D).

Furthermore, the graph intersects the x −axis on both sides of the x −axis. It means that one of the zeros is positive and the other is negative (Choice B).

2) Choice B is correct

The situation that can be represented by $y = 5x + 7$ is B. The number of people, y, in x groups of 5 people each after adding 7 more people to each group.

In this equation, $5x$ represents the original number of people in x groups of 5 people each, and the additional 7 represents the increase in the number of people in each group. Therefore, the equation calculates the total number of people, y, in x groups of 5 people each after adding 7 more people to each group.

A. The number of cookies, y, in x dozens of cookies after 7 cookies are added to each dozen. This situation does involve adding 7 to a quantity, but the equation $y = 5x + 7$ does not involve dozens of anything and does not relate to cookies.

C. The cost, y, after a \$7 discount, of buying x jackets that sell for \$5 each. In this situation, the equation should involve a discount applied to the original cost of the jackets, rather than adding 7 to the cost. The equation $y = 5x - 7$ would be more appropriate for this situation.

D. The number of inches, y, in an x-foot-tall tree after adding 7 inches to its height. This situation does involve adding 7 to a quantity (the height of the tree), but the equation $y = 5x + 7$ does not involve feet or inches and does not relate to trees.

3) Choice D is correct

Note that the factor(s) of the expression such as $f(x)$ are the zeros of the equation $f(x) = 0$. It means that, if the term $ax + b$ is the factor of f, then $f\left(-\frac{b}{a}\right) = 0$. Now, calculate the value of the expression for each option:

A. $2x + 1: 6\left(-\frac{1}{2}\right)^2 + \left(-\frac{1}{2}\right) - 2 = 6\left(\frac{1}{4}\right) + \left(-\frac{1}{2}\right) - 2 = -1$

B. $3x - 2$: $6\left(\frac{2}{3}\right)^2 + \left(\frac{2}{3}\right) - 2 = 6\left(\frac{4}{9}\right) + \left(\frac{2}{3}\right) - 2 = \frac{4}{3}$

C. $3 - 2x$: $6\left(\frac{3}{2}\right)^2 + \left(\frac{3}{2}\right) - 2 = 6\left(\frac{9}{4}\right) + \left(\frac{3}{2}\right) - 2 = \frac{26}{2}$

D. $1 - 2x$: $6\left(\frac{1}{2}\right)^2 + \left(\frac{1}{2}\right) - 2 = 6\left(\frac{1}{4}\right) + \left(\frac{1}{2}\right) - 2 = 0$

For choice D, the value of the equation is zero. So, it is the factor of the problem.

4) Choice C is correct

$(5n^2 + 4n + 8) - (n + 2 - 3n^2)$, Add like terms together: $5n^2 - (-3n^2) = 8n^2$, $4n - n = 3n$, and $8 - 2 = 6$. Combine these terms into one expression to find the answer: $(5n^2 + 4n + 8) - (n + 2 - 3n^2) = 8n^2 + 3n + 6$.

5) Choice D is correct

Write the inequality in terms of y:

$$x < \frac{5}{2}y + 5 \rightarrow x - 5 < \frac{5}{2}y \rightarrow \frac{2}{5}x - 2 < y$$

In order to plot the shaded area of the inequality of $y > \frac{2}{5}x - 2$, first, we draw the graph of the equation $y = \frac{2}{5}x - 2$ as a dashed line (choice A is not correct) on the $xy-$plane coordinate. The slope of the equation $y = \frac{2}{5}x - 2$ of the line is positive and equal to $\frac{2}{5}$. Therefore, choice B is also incorrect. Finally, we put some points (Like the origin of coordinates $(0,0)$) in the inequality to determine the correct answer.

$(0,0) \rightarrow 0 > \frac{2}{5}(0) - 2 = -2$, which is true. Therefore, the graph of choice D is the correct answer.

6) Choice D is correct

Isolate x in the equation and solve. Then:

$\frac{3}{4}(x - 2) = 3\left(\frac{1}{6}x - \frac{3}{2}\right)$, expand $\frac{3}{4}$ and 3 to the parentheses $\rightarrow \frac{3}{4}x - \frac{3}{2} = \frac{1}{2}x - \frac{9}{2}$. Add $\frac{3}{2}$ to both sides: $\frac{3}{4}x - \frac{3}{2} + \frac{3}{2} = \frac{1}{2}x - \frac{9}{2} + \frac{3}{2}$. Simplify $\frac{3}{4}x = \frac{1}{2}x - 3$. Now, subtract $\frac{1}{2}x$ from both sides: $\frac{3}{4}x - \frac{1}{2}x = \frac{1}{2}x - 3 - \frac{1}{2}x$. Simplify $\frac{1}{4}x = -3$. Multiply both sides by 4: $(4)\frac{1}{4}x = -3(4)$, simplify $x = -12$.

7) Choice A is correct

To find the inequality equivalent to $4x - 3y < 2y + 35$, we can start by isolating y on one side of the inequality:

$$4x - 3y - 2y < 2y + 35 - 2y \rightarrow 4x - 5y < 35 \rightarrow 4x - 5y - 4x < 35 - 4x$$

$$\rightarrow -5y < 35 - 4x$$

Divide both sides of the inequality by -5. So, the equivalent inequality is $y > \frac{4}{5}x - \frac{35}{5}$, which means that the answer is A. $y > 0.8x - 7$.

8) Choice C is correct

Since $x^2 + 4x + 3 = (x + 3)(x + 1)$, the fraction $x + 3 = \frac{11(x+1)}{(x^2+4x+3)}$ can be written as $x + 3 = \frac{11(x+1)}{(x+3)(x+1)}$. It is given that $x > -1$, so the common factor $x + 1$ is not equal to 0. Therefore, the fraction can be further simplified to $x + 3 = \frac{11}{(x+3)}$. Multiplying both sides of the equation by $x + 3$ gives $(x + 3)^2 = 11$. This means $x + 3$ is a number whose square is 11, so $(x + 3)$ is either $\sqrt{11}$ or $-\sqrt{11}$. Therefore, $\sqrt{11}$ is a possible value for $x + 3$.

9) Choice D is correct

Let c be the number of students in Mr. Anderson's class. The conditions described in the question can be represented by the equations $n = 3c + 5$ and $n + 21 = 4c$. Substituting $3c + 5$ for n in the second equation gives $3c + 5 + 21 = 4c$, which can be solved to find $c = 26$.

10) Choice C is correct

The area of a rectangle is calculated from the following formula:

Area = Length × Width.

Next, substitute the expressions related to the length and width of the rectangle and multiply them together:

Area $= (10 - 3x)(5x + 2) = 50x + 20 - 15x^2 - 6x = -15x^2 + 44x + 20$.

11) Choice A is correct

First, find the solutions by drawing the lines. Graph the inequality $y < 2x + 6$ by drawing a dashed line through the y-intercept $(0, 6)$ and the point $(-3, 0)$ and the solutions are all points below this line. Then, graph the inequality $y \leq \frac{1}{2}x - 2$ by drawing a line through the y-intercept $(0, -2)$ and the point $(4, 0)$, and the solution are all points below this line. The solution to the system of inequalities is the line interaction of the regions below the graphs of both lines and quadrant II contains no solutions.

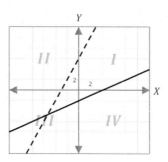

12) Choice C is correct

Use the factoring method for $h(x) = 2x^2 - 7x - 30$. To solve, you need two binomials that multiply to give $h(x)$. The constant term in each binomial must multiply to give the constant term in $h(x)$, and the coefficient of the linear term in each binomial must add up to the coefficient of the linear term in $h(x)$.

The only pair of binomials that satisfy these conditions is $(2x + 5)(x - 6)$.

We can use the distributive property to check that this is equivalent to $h(x)$:

$$(2x + 5)(x - 6) = 2x^2 - 7x - 30$$

Therefore, the answer is C.

13) Choice D is correct

Based on the graph, check each choice:

A. The y −intercept is the number of stores opened in 2005 which is the number of 100. So, it is true.

B. According to the graph, the difference in the values of the graph is increasing gradually. Since 2014, the number of stores opened will exceed 150.

C. The graph represents an exponential function in the form of $f(x) = a(b)^x$. By substituting some points on the graph, we obtained the values a and b.

$(0,100) = \big(0, f(0)\big) \rightarrow 100 = a(b)^0 \rightarrow a = 100$

$(1,125) = \big(1, f(1)\big) \rightarrow 125 = a(b)^1 \rightarrow ab = 125$

Put the value of a in the second equation and get the value of b: $b = 1.25$.

For the function $f(x) = 100(1.25)^x$, because the base of the exponential function is 1.25, we see an increase in the number of stores at a rate of 25% every year. That's true.

D. Since 25 stores were opened in the second year 2006 (Difference between 100 and 125), then this statement is incorrect and therefore the answer to the problem.

14) Choice C is correct

Moving a graph along the coordinate axes does not change the shape of the graph. Therefore, there is no change in the slope of the graph (B or D is not true!).

Next, write the equation of f by using the formula of linear function passes through two points as $y - y_1 = m(x - x_1)$, where (x_1, y_1) and (x_2, y_2) is two points in the line and m is the slope with the below formula:

$$m = \frac{y_2 - y_1}{x_2 - x_1}$$

For $(-1, -1)$ and $(2,8)$, we get:

$$m = \frac{8 - (-1)}{2 - (-1)} = 3$$

The equation of $f(x)$ is $y - 8 = 3(x - 2)$. Simplify: $y = 3x + 2$ or $f(x) = 3x + 2$.

Based on the problem data, if the graph of f was translated left 7 units to create the graph of function g. Then it can be written in the form $g(x) = f(x + 7)$.

Now, we write the equation of the graph of $g(x)$:

$g(x) = f(x + 7) \rightarrow g(x) = 3(x + 7) + 2 \rightarrow g(x) = 3x + 23$.

The y−intercept of f is 2. The y−intercept of g is 23, which is 21 units upper than 2. Choice C is the correct answer.

15) Choice A is correct

The x −intercept of a graph is the point where the line or curve intersects the x −axis. In this context, the x −axis represents the number of presentations made by the convention presenter, and the y −axis represents the number of cookies she had left to give away. Therefore, the x-intercept represents the point at which the number of presentations made by the presenter is zero, i.e., the initial state before any presentations were made. At this point, the presenter had all the cookies she started with and had not given away any yet. Hence, the x −intercept of the graph represents the initial number of cookies the presenter had before making any presentations.

16) Choice B is correct

The function $y = 20x + 50$ represents the total amount of money a customer spends on tutoring in a single month. The fixed monthly fee of $50 is represented by the constant term 50, and the hourly fee of $20 is represented by the coefficient of x, which means that for each hour of tutoring, the customer is charged $20.

Therefore, the variable x in this function represents the number of hours the customer spends on tutoring each month. The more hours the customer spends on tutoring, the higher the value of x and the higher the total cost of tutoring, represented by y.

So, the correct answer is B. The variable x represents the number of hours the customer spends on tutoring each month.

17) Choice C is correct

Let's evaluate each option using the given table:

A. $7 - 2x$

For $x = -2, f(x) = 7 - 2(-2) = 7 + 4 = 11$ (not 1.25)

For $x = 0, f(x) = 7 - 2(0) = 7$ (not 2)

For $x = 1, f(x) = 7 - 2(1) = 7 - 2 = 5$ (not 3)

For $x = 2, f(x) = 7 - 2(2) = 7 - 4 = 3$ (not 5)

B. $2x^2 + 1$

For $x = -2, f(x) = 2(-2)^2 + 1 = 2(4) + 1 = 8 + 1 = 9$ (not 1.25)

For $x = 0, f(x) = 2(0)^2 + 1 = 2(0) + 1 = 1$ (not 2)

For $x = 1, f(x) = 2(1)^2 + 1 = 2(1) + 1 = 2 + 1 = 3$ (matches the value of 3)

For $x = 2, f(x) = 2(2)^2 + 1 = 2(4) + 1 = 8 + 1 = 9$ (not 5)

C. $1 + 2^x$

For $x = -2, f(x) = 1 + 2^{-2} = 1 + \frac{1}{4} = 1.25$ (matches the value of 1.25)

For $x = 0, f(x) = 1 + 2^0 = 1 + 1 = 2$ (matches the value of 2)

For $x = 1, f(x) = 1 + 2^1 = 1 + 2 = 3$ (matches the value of 3)

For $x = 2, f(x) = 1 + 2^2 = 1 + 4 = 5$ (matches the value of 5)

D. $(x - 1)^2$

For $x = -2, f(x) = (-2 - 1)^2 = (-3)^2 = 9$ (not 1.25)

For $x = 0, f(x) = (0 - 1)^2 = (-1)^2 = 1$ (not 2)

For $x = 1, f(x) = (1 - 1)^2 = (0)^2 = 0$ (not 3)

For $x = 2, f(x) = (2 - 1)^2 = (1)^2 = 1$ (not 5)

Based on the values obtained by evaluating each option, the equation that matches the given table is C. $1 + 2^x$.

18) Choice B is correct

Let x be the number of new shoes the team can purchase. Therefore, the team can purchase $120x$. The team had $20,000 and spent $14,000. Now the team can spend on new shoes $6,000 at most. Now, write the inequality:

$120x + 14,000 \leq 20,000$.

19) Choice C is correct

The line passes through the origin. Therefore, this is a relationship of the form $d = ct$, where c is a constant representing the slope of the graph. To find the value of c, choose a point (t, d) on the graph of the line other than the origin and substitute the values of t and d into the equation. For example, if the point $(120, 40)$ is chosen, then $40 = c(120)$, and $c = \frac{1}{3}$. Therefore, the equation of the line is $d = \frac{1}{3}t$.

20) Choice D is correct

To solve this problem, we can use algebra. Let's use b to represent the number of boys in the classroom. Then the number of girls (g) is $b + 15$. We know that the total number of students is 97, so we can write: $b + g = 97 \rightarrow b + (b + 15) = 97$.

Simplifying the left side of the equation, we get

$b + b + 15 = 97 \rightarrow 2b + 15 = 97$.

Subtracting 15 from both sides, we get $2b = 82$. Dividing both sides by 2, we get: $b = 41$.

So, there are 41 boys in the classroom, and the number of girls is $41 + 15 = 56$. Therefore, the total number of girls in the classroom is 56.

21) Choice A is correct

Current formula is $A = \frac{4+w}{30}$. Multiplying each side of the equation by 30 gives $30A = 4 + w$. Subtracting 4 from each side of $30A = 4 + w$ gives $w = 30A - 4$.

22) Choice A is correct

To determine which set of ordered pairs represents x as a function of y, we need to check whether each value of x corresponds to only one value of y in the set. In other words, we need to check if each x is repeated with different values of y or not.

Option A has each value of x corresponding to only one value of y, so it represents x as a function of y. Therefore, the answer is A. $\{(-9,2), (0,6,), (1, -2,), (-3,6,)\}$.

Option B has $x = -1$ repeated with different values of y, so it does not represent x as a function of y.

Option C has $x = 3$ and $x = -4$ repeated with different values of y, so it does not represent x as a function of y.

Option D has $x = 2$ repeated with different values of y equal to 3 and 4, so it does not represent x as a function of y.

23) Choice A is correct

The y−intercept of a graph is the point where the graph intersects the y−axis. To find the y−intercept of the graph of $g(x) = 0.7(2.3)^x$, substitute $x = 0$ in the equation:

$$g(0) = 0.7(2.3)^0 = 0.7$$

Therefore, the y−intercept of the graph of $g(x)$ is $(0,0.7)$. The value of the y−intercept is 0.7.

Keystone Algebra I Practice Tests 10 Explanations
Section 2

24) The answer is 40

Let x represent the number of correct answers from the player and y represents the number of incorrect answers from the player. Since the player answered 50 questions in total, the equation $x + y = 50$ represents this situation. Also, since the score is found by subtracting the number of incorrect answers from three times the number of correct answers and the player received a score of 110, the equation $3x - y = 110$ represents this situation. Adding the system of two equations together yields $(x + y) + (3x - y) = 50 + 110$. This can be rewritten as $4x = 160$. Finally, solving for x by dividing both sides of the equation by 4 yields $x = 40$.

25) The answer is 0

The value of $f(-4)$ is equal to the value of $f(x)$, or y when $x = -4$. The graph indicates that when $x = -4$, $y = 0$. It follows that value of $f(-4) = 0$.

26) The answer is 17

Number 125 can be written in exponential form $h^{\frac{k}{6}}$, where h and k are positive integers as follows: $5^{\frac{18}{6}}, 25^{\frac{9}{6}}, 125^{\frac{6}{6}}, (125^2)^{\frac{3}{6}}, (5^9)^{\frac{2}{6}}, (5^{18})^{\frac{1}{6}}$. Hence, if $h^{\frac{k}{6}} = 125$ where h and k are positive integers, then $\frac{k}{6}$ can be $3, \frac{3}{2}, 1, \frac{1}{2}, \frac{1}{3}$ or $\frac{1}{6}$. So, the value of k can be, $18, 9, 6, 3, 2,$ or 1. Any of these values may be gridded as the correct answer. Now subtract 1 from 18: $18 - 1 = 17$.

27) The answer is $\frac{3}{2}$ **or** 1.5

It's given that the system of linear equations has no solutions. Therefore, the lines represented by the two equations are parallel. Each of the equations can be written in slope-intercept form, or $y = mx + b$, where m is the slope of the line and b is the y-coordinate of the line's y-intercept. Subtracting $\frac{3}{4}x$ from both sides of

$\frac{3}{4}x - \frac{1}{2}y = 12$ yields $-\frac{1}{2}y = -\frac{3}{4}x + 12$. Dividing both sides of this equation by $-\frac{1}{2}$ yields $y = \frac{-\frac{3}{4}}{-\frac{1}{2}}x + \frac{12}{-\frac{1}{2}}$, or $y = \frac{3}{2}x - 24$. Therefore, the slope of the line represented by the first equation in the system is $\frac{3}{2}$. The second equation in the system can be put into a slope-intercept form by first subtracting the ax from both sides of $ax - by = 9$, then dividing both sides of the equation by $-b$, which yields $y = \frac{a}{b}x - \frac{9}{b}$. Therefore, the slope of the line represented by the second equation in the system is $\frac{a}{b}$. Parallel lines have equal slopes. Therefore, $\frac{a}{b} = \frac{3}{2}$. Either $\frac{3}{2}$ or 1.5 may be entered as the correct answer.

Effortless Math's Keystone Algebra I Online Center

Effortless Math Online Keystone Algebra I Center offers a complete study program, including the following:

✓ Step-by-step instructions on how to prepare for the Keystone Algebra I test

✓ Numerous Keystone Algebra I worksheets to help you measure your math skills

✓ Complete list of Keystone Algebra I formulas

✓ Video lessons for all Keystone Algebra I topics

✓ Full-length Keystone Algebra I practice tests

✓ And much more…

No Registration Required.

Visit **EffortlessMath.com/KeystoneAlgebra1** to find your online Keystone Algebra I resources.

Receive the PDF version of this book or get another FREE book!

Thank you for using our Book!

Do you LOVE this book?

Then, you can get the PDF version of this book or another book absolutely FREE!

Please email us at:

info@EffortlessMath.com

for details.

Author's Final Note

I hope you enjoyed completing this practice book. You've made it through the book! Great job!

I would like to express my sincere appreciation for choosing this book to help you prepare for your Keystone Algebra I test. With a plethora of options available, I am grateful that you selected this practice book.

It took me years to write this practice book for the Keystone Algebra I because I wanted to prepare a comprehensive Keystone Algebra I practice book to help students make the most effective use of their valuable time while preparing for the test.

Over the course of my decade-long career teaching and tutoring math, I have compiled my personal notes and experiences into the creation of this book. It is my fervent hope that the information and practice tests contained within these pages will assist you in achieving success on your Keystone Algebra I exam.

If you have any questions, please contact me at reza@effortlessmath.com and I will be glad to assist. Your feedback will help me to greatly improve the quality of my books in the future and make this book even better. Furthermore, I expect that I have made a few minor errors somewhere in this book. If you think this to be the case, please let me know so I can fix the issue as soon as possible.

If you enjoyed this book and found some benefit in using it, I'd like to hear from you and hope that you could take a quick minute to post a review on the book's Amazon page.

I personally go over every single review, to make sure my books really are reaching out and helping students and test takers. Please help me help Algebra students, by leaving a review!

I wish you all the best in your future success!

Reza Nazari

Math teacher and author

Made in United States
North Haven, CT
16 April 2024

51394470R00154